THE THIN LINE
EVERYTHING AND NOTHING

Hannah Storm has spent most of the last two decades travelling the world as a journalist, experiences which have shaped and inspired her flash fiction and non-fiction. As well as writing whenever she can, she works as a media consultant, trainer and facilitator, specialising in gender, safety, mental health and leadership. She lives in Yorkshire with her Kiwi husband and two children. This is her debut personal collection. She is also working on a memoir and finalising a novel. In any spare time left, Hannah is an avid runner, having clocked up around twenty marathons.

The Thin Line Between Everything and Nothing

Hannah Storm

REFLEX PRESS

First published as a collection in 2021 by Reflex Press
Abingdon, Oxfordshire, OX14 3SY
www.reflex.press

A CIP catalogue record of this book is
available from the British Library.

ISBN: 978-1-914114-02-1

1 3 5 7 9 10 8 6 4 2

Printed and bound in Great Britain
by Imprint Digital

Cover image by Julie Cowdy

www.reflex.press/the-thin-line-
between-everything-and-nothing/

To Terry, Azara and Rafferty, with love.
And to those who have been silenced,
in solidarity.

CONTENTS

Sarajevo Rose

Damir buys a bouquet once a month at Chelsea Market. Seven long-stemmed roses. Always red. He hands the flower-seller ten bucks, watches her count the change into his palm – nickels, quarters, pennies.

Now he can tell the coins apart, but there was a time he couldn't. He remembers that first day when the change slipped from his grasp, ricocheting like shrapnel. They both ducked to the cobbles, rising together so he could not resist her gaze.

'They say life spins on a dime,' she said, returning the smallest silver. He nodded, but all he understood was that her eyes were blue like a Sarajevo summer sky, and when she said 'dime', it sounded like his name.

Back home, 'Damir' meant peace. Here it meant scorn, it meant stranger, it meant the soiled sheets of a bedsit he could scarcely afford, in a building shaken by each passing train.

The roses stand in a soda bottle on the window ledge. His only luxury – even the bottle was borrowed from the bum downstairs. Damir never considers going without them, and when winter comes, he wears all his clothes to reduce the bills so he can still visit the market.

On his way to the flower-seller, he remembers a day in Markhale with his sister, her hand slippery with a seven-year-old's excitement. The hills around Sarajevo had been quiet. He remembers a young woman dropping a single, precious coin. Damir ducked to retrieve it. She did too. He remembers her sky-blue eyes. He doesn't remember dropping his sister's hand. The building shook with the blast. When he looked up, his sister was gone.

Damir has read how Sarajevans painted red roses in the shell's concrete scars. When his flowers wilt, the petals fall to the floor. Damir never picks them up.

Behind the Mountains,
More Mountains

The first time Maman got sick, Marie climbed to the top of the tallest place she knew. From there, she could gaze out over the water, as blue as the sky in those final moments before the clouds turned grey and the rain came. From the top of her lookout, eyes cast forward, she imagined she was a queen, or better still a king. *Don't look down, Marie,* Maman had told her in the days when she was still well, in the days when the two of them would sit selling *bannan* in the market of Cité Soleil. *Never look down. Only up. Deye mon, gen mon. Behind the mountains, there are more mountains.*

When Maman was too sick to look up to see the white clouds ribboning the sky, Marie would tell her the words she had learnt at her knee. *Dye mon, gen mon.* By then, Maman could scarcely raise her head, and her eyes, once the colour of the precious cacao beans, were now like the milky, muddy puddles of water around the trash mountains Marie had once climbed as her castle. Now she would spend her days collecting the wood rejected by those who stripped the hillsides above the city, always making sure she got home before dark to light a fire by her mother's side.

After the fires went out, when their light and warmth was a memory like Maman, and the men came, Marie closed her eyes even though it was already dark. *Cité Soleil* means *Sun City*, but here night had fallen long ago, and power cuts were a life sentence to those who lived without power of any kind. Nobody heard Marie when she cried. Nobody came when her cries turned to screams, when she shouted *Maman, Maman,* when she dug her fingers into her skin, imagining the peaks that towered above the other peaks, when she smelt the sourness of the men's breath, the same sweet sickly smell that rose from the debris of other people's lives that had once been her castle and her sanctuary. Nobody helped her find water to wash the wounds that she might have wiped. In the stinking streams that severed Cité Soleil, the water had dried up, and the bodies of others like her lay rotting in the ruins of her country. In the darkness, she could smell and sense her childhood ebbing away.

When the earth first started to shake, Marie knew she needed to get to higher ground. She knew there were mountains beyond mountains, but hers was a country of high peaks, and she didn't trust the low land lapped by the water. As a child, these paths had been part of her. She had known each crevasse and contour of the land that rose from the cobalt Caribbean to the matching blue sky. She had hiked the naked strips of land, carrying firewood for charcoal to keep Maman warm. The baskets of branches had always felt heavy then, but nothing like the weight she carried now.

Towards the top of one rise, Marie stumbled. There a solitary tree clung to the fractured land, half lifted from the soil, its roots spread out like bony fingers clinging to a cliff, the fine digits of someone holding onto something where nothing else remained. Marie knew she had to stop. She knew that beyond this rise, there would be another and another. She counted them coming and going. *Dye mon, gen mon. Dye mon, gen mon. Dye mon, gen mon.*

In the shadow of the tree, in the parched and arid dirt, on the hillside above her collapsed country, surrounded by the roots and ruins of the past, she gave birth to a daughter, the child of men, the child of a history and country she would never really know. Marie looked down at her baby and named her Christela, after her mother. *Christela*, meaning Christ is here.

No Woman's Land

The airport roof is a no man's land. I sort the papers for the evening news. There's nowhere to hide from the heat or the hypocrisy.

To my left, a village of tarpaulin skirts the runway. There, grey bird-beaked planes line up along the buckled tarmac. Trestle tables are pregnant under provisions. Men in fatigues rest on canvas chairs, sheltered from the sun by monster marquees. They smoke, play cards, throw dice and dark humour, staving off the boredom of waiting and the trauma of witnessing.

A man wearing a crew cut and combats walks by, a can of Dr Pepper in one hand, a satellite phone in the other. I interviewed him earlier, when he reeled responses to the camera that said nothing and told me everything. Now he's smiling – talking to his kids, perhaps – hearing about their school day, their softball game, their weekend plans.

'Pop misses you,' I imagine him crooning, when the wind whips his words across the wasted land.

He no longer seems to notice the boxes by the runway. They have been there since I arrived three days ago, growing higher, going nowhere. The ground shimmers like an oasis. I wish the boxes were a mirage.

But still the planes keep landing. And when they do, in marches an army of uniformed ants to pull out the packages and pile them here and there, wherever there's space. Anywhere but where it's really needed, I think, raising my head above the partition before I'm knocked back by the power of another plane. Adrenalin surges through my body, and it feels like an aftershock.

I force myself further into the concrete, tighten my grip on the papers that hold my words to the world.

When I raise my head again, it's to look to the right, where a high stone fence skirts a factory long fallen into disrepair.

I'd pleaded with the peacekeepers to let me inside. But once past its rusted gates, it was hard to tell where the walls of the broken building began and where they ended, what was the result of disrepair or disaster, what collapsed in years and what collapsed in seconds. Empty cans and broken bottles, piles of rubbish, shreds of material stained in blood, all were thrown into stinking, shining relief by the unseasonal winter sun.

Even the trees were skeletal, but on their fragile limbs, people clung to life. A bag of saline hung from a branch over a small girl, her left leg twice the size of her right. It was splinted by a chair leg, and she lay on a wooden door balanced on two metal drums.

In the shade cast by the tree and the doors sat a young woman. On her lap lay a tiny bundle: a baby delivered in the dust.

The saline was running low in the bag above her. Some had spilt onto the good leg of the older child, a path in the pale skin.

Saltwater tears streaked the grey mask of the woman's face. She didn't move when one plane flew overhead, or the next.

I followed its arc as it disappeared, but the promise of its aid reaching her was as elusive as a rainbow's pot of gold.

Back on the tarmac, the men play at dice like gods, deciding who lives and dies.

I write and rewrite my script on the scraps of paper I'll use to tell of the baby born in the dust as her older sister lay dying.

It's just minutes before I go on air, before the lights of London send me live. There's another noise, a clang of metal and toll of heavy voices and three pairs of boots marching across no man's land.

'I'm afraid we can no longer guarantee your safety, ma'am. We need to ask you to leave,' says Dr Pepper. I nod, knowing his polite entreaties are political excuses. I pick up my papers, swallow my words. I'll obey his orders, though I don't believe them.

And I'll leave the airport, but it won't ever leave me.

Bulletproof

When I go to war, they loan me a flak jacket, a big blue thing designed for men. It squashes my shoulders, metal plates pinning flat my chest, breasts yielding to the weight of them. Androgenised.

But I wear the body armour because I'm told it will keep me safe if someone shoots from a distance. I wear it because I'm told these are cheaper than the ones for women. I wear it because I'm told there are more male journalists on the frontline than women, because men are better at the warry stuff, and women more lightweight. I wear it because I don't want to rock the boat and give the news desk another reason not to send me to do this job. I wear it because I've told them I am the best 'man' for the job. I wear it because I want to be part of the solution and not part of the problem, as if my gender might be classed as anything else.

I wear it because the man in the equipment stores, deep in the belly of the building, where they keep the cameras, tripods and satellite phones, the team first aid kits, generators and batteries, looked me up and down, handed me the canvas bag with the body armour and a helmet, and whistled through his yellow teeth.

'We don't get many girls going to war.' He stank of fags and coffee, held out a cracked biro in his fat, stained fingers.

'I've checked the plates. They need to come back exactly as they are. Sign here.' I pressed the pen hard and left an imprint on the desk.

Now I sit by the wall in the bowels of another building, where the stores have been looted, where nothing remains but rubble and the smell of shit and fear and sweat and how long will this last and I wonder if the scar of my name will still be there when I get back. I hear the crack of gunfire and remember what he told me – that if I could still hear it, I would be fine.

The whistles and whines get closer, and the ground starts to shake, but I wonder if it is just me shaking in my too-big turtle shell which creeps up my body and covers my mouth, muddling my senses, exposing my womb to the world.

I am silence.

I hear the sound of boots and deep voices, checking the doors. Opening, closing, opening, closing. I cross my legs, pull my helmet down to hide my face, hope the jacket shields my gender. I know none of this body armour will protect me if these men target me point-blank.

An Eye to Keep Them Safe at Sea

I pocket a smooth stone. I'll learn to skim it this time. It sits in my palm, warm like a living thing.

The fading sun has flattened the landscape. It's quiet, only the cicadas and the sea surface my memories.

When I was little, my parents brought us to Lesbos every summer. Lunch in the taverna by the bay. While Mum and Dad toasted their fortune with ouzo, Manos, the taverna owner, knew exactly how to keep us happy. He brought me and Matty baklava, and we would cradle each sweet, brittle layer in our mouths until they melted. We were left picking the nuts from our teeth, swinging our legs over the harbour wall. There we watched the men moor their blue and white boats, each painted with an eye to keep them safe at sea.

They'd unload their nets, splashing fish like silver shards into wooden crates, and Matty would watch me watching them. It would be the same scene every day, and every day my little sister would gawp at me and giggle through gums glued with Greek honey. Her eyes were as wide as the ones on the boats when I whispered the stories of the ancient gods.

There was one tale she would ask for again and again: the one about the goddess who watched over sailors. She saved Odysseus, wrapping him in her shawl after his boat was wrecked by Poseidon. Before she became immortal, her name was Ino, and she was a real-life princess. And to Matty, that was even more exciting than being a goddess.

Because she was still only small, I didn't tell Matty the bit about how Ino had thrown herself and her child into the sea to escape her husband when Hera turned him crazy. I didn't tell her that after she drowned, her name wasn't Ino anymore. Leucothea was hard enough for me to say aged twelve. At four, Matty had no chance. Still she loved the name Ino, and whenever she heard it, Matty would cackle with laughter and say, 'I know, I know,' even though she didn't know.

When she got bored of listening, and I got bored of telling stories, we would clamber down off the rocky boulders and jagged stones to the shale that slipped beneath my bare feet, and I'd squeal when the water tickled my toes. Matty ran into the water without hesitation, forever wanting to see how far we could go before we could no longer touch the stony floor.

~

In my pocket, I tighten my grip around the one stone, wondering how long it took to surface from the waters. Memories mist my eyes, my mind. Darkness blurs the corners. I push the stone down further, start to run. But night comes fast. The village lights are pinpricks. My phone's torch spins a shadow across the path.

I can hear sea, cicadas. I remember the crystal clink as Manos would pour my parents one last ouzo and the '*yamas!*' that used to signal all was well in the world.

Then the screams.

I run faster, heading for the harbour. But I don't recognise this place anymore. Thirty years have changed more than just me.

Shards of shale rub my toes. I run, slip, run, slip, slip. My front foot hits something, jolts me, and I fall, shielding my phone, not my body. My right palm stings. I touch my knee, blood through torn trousers.

I know the tide is coming in, and I want to shout to Matty to come back, but it's no use. I clasp my nose, inhale the metal of blood, not memory. I feel in my pocket. I've lost my stone. There's no way I'll find it now. I could use my dying torch to search for the one in a million.

No. It's too late.

My phone flickers, catches the edge of something: a collection of cast-off clothing? A towel from a drunk tourist? A pile of the orange and black life jackets found along this coast now?

I edge closer. There are two tiny feet tucked underneath. Closer, still. Blood pulses my ears. I bend down, not too close. There are tendrils of hair, a face pale in the arc of phone light. I turn it away. Of course. The child is asleep. It is long past her bedtime. But what a strange place to sleep. Half on her haunches, head to one side, she looks peaceful. I daren't shine the light too close in case I wake her. Don't be so ridiculous. Who would let their child sleep here? Mum and Dad would never have left us alone on the beach, and she's much younger than I was then. It's getting cold now; I wonder if she is. The stones will keep her warm for now, and I don't want to disturb her. But just in case, I reach into my rucksack, pull out my pashmina and lay it carefully over her. She is smaller than I thought, and it easily covers her body twice. Do I lift her head and fashion a pillow? No, I don't want to disturb her. I'll lie beside her until she wakes. She'll be scared and want her mum. I'll help her find her when morning comes.

And yet she's so quiet. All I can hear is my own breathing, fast and shallow. Someone starts crying. The darkness answers with the distant howl of a dog. When she was tiny, and I thought I was so much older than I really was, Matty was terrified of dogs. Dogs and the dark.

I close my eyes, imagine the boats, their eyes wide, watching over the people on the water.

'Don't worry, little one. I'm here. I'm here.'

Playing God

The streets are steeper than I remember. When I was a kid, I charged up these cobbled paths, picking my way along the network of warrens as if I had some sixth sense.

I was always the first one to the top, and I'd sit, smug as a creamed-up cat, chanting the words to *I'm the King of the Castle*, until my sister and cousin arrived, red-faced and furious. Of course, it didn't last. Not the honeyed baklava I handed out to buy back their friendship. Not the taunting rhythms of *you dirty rascal*, fired like arrows from my fairy tale fortress. None of it.

The shutters are closed now, protecting the locals from the heat, protecting me from the glare of a generation raised with *Why didn't you?* and *I told you* and aged with *Is that really her?*

I cling to the shadows, my headscarf shading me from the sun and the shame of their shuttered mouths. But she's there. In the young woman in white with her heavy bag. In the child crying behind the closed windows. In the amber shells of the houses that haven't changed. In the wisteria that hangs over my head and fills my nostrils with sibling shame.

From the top of the hill, Turkey looks close enough to touch. I reach out my hand, remember that first day when Papa told us how the sun always made things look closer than they were. How he and my uncle used to race up to this place, to pretend they were heroes of old, brave men who pleased the gods and proved they were worthy of immortality.

My little sister marvelled when she heard how they had swum across the strait, almost to the foreign shore. She didn't hear the part of the tale where hubris made them human, and they were saved by a boat, painted with a blue eye to keep people safe at sea. My cousin and I were old enough to know better, but my sister was only four. To her, we were players in a fairy tale that was supposed to end with a happily ever after.

There's a cool wind up here. I yank my pashmina under my nose, feel how fast and hot my breath is, from the running, the remembering. Seagulls spin on the thermals, stretching their wings from one world to another. Their screams sound like the last panicked sounds before silence, and I shudder when they cast shadows across the sun. I watch one of the birds tumble to the foam and see beneath its falling arrow something bobbing in the darkening blue. I watch the bird and the thing disappear beneath a wave, and then rise again, disappear, then rise.

I abandon my scarf and run. I know now that you can't reach the water from here in the time it takes a person to drown. I know now that no painted eye will ever keep people safe at sea.

Lesser Known Facts About Sloths

'In Spanish, the sloth is called *oso perezoso*.' You are reading from an Amazon travel guide, your limbs stretching across the sofa to the polished Peruvian mahogany table. I want to tell you to move your filthy feet from my friend's furniture.

'It means lazy bear,' I say, knowing the truth. They're not bears, or lazy, rarely sleeping more than ten hours. But you're not listening.

'Did you know sloths only shit once a week?' You reach for one of the beers lined up on the table because you're too lazy to go to the fridge. 'And they shit out a third of their body weight.'

There are two kinds of sloth, this much I know. The two-toed and the three-toed. One can turn its head 360 degrees. I stick my middle finger up at you, relieved you can't spin your head right now.

I smell the beer leaking onto the Quechua carpet. I've reached the kitchen, grabbed a towel, soaked it, wrung it out, brought it to you and rescued the book before you're even upright. You stretch out an arm, and for a second, I imagine you are two-fingered.

Sloths have a symbiotic relationship with algae. Their absorbent fur gives the algae shelter and water; in return, it provides camouflage. When we first met, you were obsessed with wearing camo, or DPM as you called it in the army. You said you'd got used to sleeping in a hammock in a tree, and sometimes I'd come back to yours in my lunch break to find you hanging there asleep in your greens.

You've been doing much the same since you got here. You told me you'd missed me so much you decided to surprise me with a two-week visit. When the fortnight was up, you admitted you were between jobs and would look when you got home. 'I needed a break,' you said, suggesting the jungle. 'I've always wanted to swim in the Amazon.'

Sloths can move three times faster in water than on land. I suspect the same could be said of you.

I pour myself a glass of wine, wonder what I'm doing here in my mate's apartment, with this layabout who shows me as much affection as a sloth shows its mate.

We've only had sex once in the fortnight that became four weeks, then six. That was two weeks ago in our ecolodge near Puerto Maldonado, after we had finally seen a real sloth.

In bed tonight, I'll hold my breath and count to forty. The number of seconds a sloth can hold her breath. The number of years a sloth can live. Then I'll walk through to where you're drinking your beer and tell you it is over.

Later I will dream of giving birth upside down.

Tomorrow I will wake to the early morning Lima-grey in an empty apartment. On the table, the Amazon guide will lie open, one sentence underlined informing me sloths can retain their grip after death.

Game Over

I'm first to play. Loosen the ties, plunge my hand deep into the bag. Pluck seven letters from inside. I pull out an A first: one point, then S – always useful for making something singular a plural, but a lazy way to gain the advantage. Then T. I, L, O, and E follow. It's not a great hand. Even with the advantage of going first, crossing the double word score, it won't amount to much. I place the tiles on the plastic holder, move them around, consider my options.

SAIL – *to move along or travel over water.* Remember that first time? Looking out from the glass-fronted lobby, beneath chandeliers that hang like constellations, you point at the boats bobbing on the water. We agree we'd both rather be out there looking at the stars, sailing on the sea, instead of in this generic hotel at another bloody work conference.

LATE – *after the usual or proper time.* Late that evening in the bar, long after our colleagues go to bed, you confess you can't sail, and I tell you I can't either. Not that it matters.

SIT – *be or remain in a particular position or state.* For this conference and every future one – in cities around the world – we sit each night, talking. Sometimes the others try to join us, but we know we're the only ones who really know the rules. One night you suggest a board game. 'We're less likely to be disturbed,' you say, reaching for a Scrabble set stacked away behind books leafed by other lives.

LAST – *occurring or coming after all the others.* Since the first day we met, we have known this will be the last. Each time we meet in future, we will know there will be one final time. Right now, this is the first of those lasts. I follow you to your room, and between sheets that have seen many stories, we explore our pasts and our futures.

EAST – *a cardinal point on the compass, equidistant at ninety degrees between north and south.* I watch the sun rise through the curtains of your room, left open so we could map the stars and remind each other that the same constellations will shine above our heads no matter the physical distance between us.

AIL – *to cause, or to feel, pain.* There is an emptiness that I cannot shake; an all-consuming ache that haunts me as I kiss you one last time at the airport, and we head to our separate gates. It happens every time we say goodbye, every time we go back to our individual lives, after every conference, work meeting, excuse we make to spend time together.

AISLE – *a walkway between; as in a plane, or church.* Through the air, we both fly, and that narrow space grows and grows until in a small matter of hours, we are worlds apart; you back to your life and I to mine. I cling to what you told me between those sheets, how you wish we could have done this differently.

STEAL – *to move secretly or unobserved.* By day, by night, we text, we steal precious moments to talk when nobody else can hear us.

LOSE – *to come to be without.* Your children are grown, mine are still at home. Whole years pass when we don't see each other. Then out of the blue, you text to tell me there's something I need to know.

LOST – *no longer to be found; being something, or someone that something or someone has failed to win.* We meet. You are the same, but different. You tell me I haven't changed. I cannot bring myself to say the same. As we kiss, you pass me a box wrapped in paper, make me promise not to open it until after you've gone.

SO, I, SAT... TALE. This is our tale, where it ends. Even now, it's hard to find the right words.

And then I see it, the one I have missed this whole time: the word that will give me fifty extra points because I've managed to use all my tiles.

I lay the little squares down carefully, I-S-O-L-A-T-E.

ISOLATE – *cause to be or remain alone or apart from others.*

As I reach for the tiles, they scatter on the board you bought me, consonants and vowels separating.

I order the vowels in front of me: A, E, I, O. No U.

The Huntsman

We're slow dancing to Bryan Adams. He can't understand the song, the boy with his hands on my bum. But I can.

I pull away, look into his eyes, like the words tell me. They dazzle in the disco ball. He pulls me closer.

His lips slide across my face like a snail, and he tastes of garlic. When I gasp for air, I breathe in body odour.

We move apart when the song stops. It still has a few more weeks at number one. But long after it has slipped from the charts, it will pin itself to my memories like Robin Hood's arrows.

I am fourteen, and this is my first French exchange. It's also my first French kiss. That sounds so much better than snogging. If it weren't for the garlic snail, it would almost be perfect, especially since it happened during the theme tune to my favourite film.

If I am Maid Marian, my prince of thieves is Sylvain, the cousin of my school exchange partner Aurelie. Her father is a huntsman, and they live in a cottage on the edge of France's own Sherwood Forest.

I wake the next morning, lyrics of lust in my head. I foot-step across the floorboard to dreams of beautiful maidens and handsome heroes. I throw open the wooden shutters to my own fairy tale forest.

Spilt blood stains the decking. I smell flesh and hear flies. Strips of sunlight sharpen the dark bristles.

I creep down the wooden stairs to the kitchen, toe-tapping to musical memories. Smell hits before sight. The metal tang of fresh blood, the fat, misshapen flesh of the beast straddled across the kitchen table. The family cat mews from beneath folds of meat that drip dark juice onto the tiled floor.

It's the same table we sat at yesterday, dunking our brioche into tepid bowls of drinking chocolate. The same we'll sit at tomorrow when I'll scour the wood for dark patches where the blood seeped in.

'*Un sanglier*, Sarah.' They laugh at my look of horror. I know the local delicacy is wild boar, but it's the first time I've seen one like this.

Foreign laughter follows me stumbling through shuttered shadows. Heave open the wooden door, and I am blinded by light. He's there staring at me, Sylvain. It's as if by fending off the hounds, I've found myself in front of the huntsman.

He pulls me towards him, twists my wrist, tries to kiss me in the street. I wrench from his grip, trip inside, past the table, blood still dripping on the floor.

There's a door that I dive for, throw myself in, locking the toilet behind me. Two huge eyes terrified in the tiny mirror over the moulding sink. He's coaxing me, trying to draw me from my den.

Laughter in the background, and I imagine them stabbing, slicing, finally stewing the dead animal.

Then there's a flash of knife down the side of the door. I pray the lock will hold. It appears again, shining metal against the tiled floor. Blade bloodied from the prey.

36

YOLO*

In the army, everything is abbreviated. TLAs you call them. Three letter acronyms. You wear them like uniform, body armour, these codes shield you in civvy street. Like PDAs. You only permit displays of affection in public when they serve you. Then you brandish me like the trophy you still buff, displayed proudly on your cabinet with your last regiment photo. You were already FUBAR by then: fucked up beyond all recognition. This is five words, you remind me, as if I can't 'fucking' count, as if I don't know the rule of three has been applied rhetorically throughout history by those who like to think they are great orators. As if it is you who has the Oxford degree, not me. I learn quickly, rules are meant to be broken, like hearts and dreams and people's lives. So, when you churn out TLAs as excuses for your behaviour – MOD, POC, FOB, IED – as if you are still at war, they land like shrapnel, and I take cover, to protect myself. Your only concession to any number other than three, are the seven Ps. You cling to them as if together they provide the silver bullet. I learn in its absence the meaning of PPE, embrace the less conventional version of KISS. Keep it simple, stupid. I am fighting my own war. I

---

*You only live once; cf. YODO, you only die once.

unravel these seven letters, now you have gone AWOL. Prior planning and preparation prevent piss poor performance. WTF. Who's counting? Seven, three, or five. Ours was SNAFU, situation normal, all fucked up.

Mother of Gold

Tio Pablo is waiting for me in the market square of Madre de Dios. His rubber lips part to gold-plated teeth. His serpent tongue flicks a line of spit across his stubbled cheek, and when he pulls me close to kiss, he smells of coca leaves and liquor.

'You're to stay with me,' he says, before telling me to call him Tio, or uncle.

'Any family of Miguel's is family of mine.'

Tio flings my bag on his back with the strength of a man half his age. I feel in my pocket for Mother's rosary.

'You can pay me later. For now, they need you at work.'

Tio leads me through the snaking streets, past the port busy with boats that take away the bullion. I try to ignore the young women in tight Lycra tops and miniskirts, who hiss at me through red lips split by rotten teeth.

There's no sun in the basement bar, and in the dark, I can't spot the Virgin Mary.

That night after I have brushed away the bottles and the bodies of miners who think they can buy me like beer, I walk back through the same streets now empty of the hissing women. I creep up the stairs, pull off my tight top and skirt, climb into the bed and reach for my rosary.

I wake to a door opening, a beam of light across my bed, blinding, a familiar smell, and for a second, I think I'm back home. Until Tio staggers in.

'I've come to take payment, Maria.' His words wobble with drink and desire. I clutch my rosary tighter, shaking too.

'*Madre*,' I whisper, unsure if I'm calling for my mother or the virgin. Pablo laughs. 'She can't help you now. That's why you're here, Maria.'

His hand is on my mouth, metal smell. The rosary slips from my fingers onto the floor. I hear it smash, see beads rolling towards the golden dawn.

Please Look Out for This Bear

'They're the only ones now living in South America,' you tell me, reaching gently for my glasses.

'In Aymara and Quechua, they're called *Jukumari*. Spectacled bear just doesn't have the same appeal, does it?' You smile, wiping the smudges from my lenses, hold them up to the light to make sure you've caught all the smears, then settle them back across the bridge of my nose.

Now you are so close, I can smell the sweetness of the coca leaves that we've both been chewing to ward off the altitude sickness. I still feel lightheaded. Even though you're used to the Andean air, you swear by these sacred leaves of the Incas.

'The bears are vulnerable these days,' you whisper, as we weave our way down darkened corridors. 'They have been hunted, and their natural habitat stripped away.'

I follow you, out the back of the hotel you recently renovated, high above the tourist town of Aguas Calientes, trying to trust the path you take, my feet clawing at cobbles rubbed smooth by decades of tourists treading these stones by day.

We pass the gift shop with Paddington Bears lined like security guards in its windows, then the empty ticket booth where visitors can pause for a picture with the country's most famous furry export. 'Are you sure this is okay?' I hesitate, as you creep past the gates that bar our entry.

The night sings with the sound of native birds. I inhale the thick smell of rare orchids that were reintroduced recently, long after they were almost wiped out by the men who came to map these hidden parts.

'They build their nests in trees,' you say, but I don't ask if you mean the birds, or the bears, or even those who came to pillage these lands.

Up here, the air might be thin, but the sky is thick with stars, whose stories thread their way through the fables of Pachamama, the earth mother and each and every one of her Inca descendants – down to Pachakutiq. I've read the guide-books and know he is the emperor for whom this place was supposedly built, and we've already joked that his name meant 'he who moves earth and heaven'.

Here it's easy to imagine why these people worshipped the world that rises up from the foaming waters of the Urubamba, through the cordillera, into the cloud forest, to the humid jungle walls we now inhale beneath the starry heavens.

You stop, and in the darkness, I see you reach a finger to your mouth. I move closer to you, searching for signs. You scoop your hand under my foot, no longer slippery on stones. I am rooted as you lift me up and over the wall and into this sacred city. Now the moon casts its light across the stage in front of us, and I see rising from the lunar lamp the jagged crest of Huayna Picchu.

The wind whips around us, magnifying the murmur from below. We seek sanctuary in the low branches of a tree, listening to the sound of the river snaking its way through the canyon. I listen for the grunts and huffs of the spectacled bear, but there is nothing but the sound of heaven and earth moving further apart.

There Are Twenty Million People in New York, but Tonight We Are the Only Two

It's been two hours since Google Maps glued us together.

'What if there's something I need to tell you,' you say, your fingers lacing mine.

'I know.' I've known since the last time we were together, when you told me you loved me. I didn't say the words then, and now I wonder if it would have made any difference. But you knew it.

'I love every bit of you. I always have.' You had kissed away my insecurities then on someone else's Egyptian cotton sheets.

In New York, every street corner holds a story. Here on 45th and Broadway, we share ours. These are the places and sounds that have featured in films and songs that promise something we can't have. And yet, here we write our own words and record our own scenes.

'I know,' I tell you, as those three words break all the promises I've made.

Time never stops. Not here. Neon lights, theatres that turn love and loss into entertainment, flicker above our heads.

This is their stage. This is ours.

Later you kiss away my worries again, and I slip into sleep. I dream of a baby born to a woman who isn't me. I wake to an empty room, sirens shrieking like the wails of a newborn, to an empty womb and to a city full of you.

How Not to Make a Birth Plan

Ride through the rain because the car won't start. Get soaked by the old people driving too close to you and the kerb. Hurtle down the identikit corridors, your husband's yellow bike jacket dripping water on the floor. Watch the women with pearls and pinched faces, and wonder if they are tutting at you or the queue at the hospital they come to each week with their husbands, who turn to them with deaf ears and *Daily Mails*.

When it's your turn to be seen, watch the midwife prod your belly: 'You still planning that water birth?' She scribbles in your notes. Watch the pinched faces turn to smiles then pull on your husband's jacket again to go into battle.

Repeat after four weeks, when you're too big for the bike. Try to follow the midwife's advice to 'relax', even though you're on a trolley with someone's fingers in your fanny, feeling for something they can't find.

'He's sideways,' she says; you don't hear the 'don't worry'. She sends you to another hospital where they scan your son, and you joke that he must be confused about which way is up: after all, his dad is a Kiwi.

Repeat at thirty-seven, thirty-eight weeks. Try not to panic when they say don't worry.

At thirty-nine, forty, forty-one weeks, listen when the midwife says second babies rarely engage before labour. Try to relax. Fail.

Wake a week later with the rush of warm water. Watch as your husband carries your older child to the car, thinking how small she looks asleep. 'Don't worry, darling,' you say, more for you than her. Wait for the first pains. Short. Manageable.

Spend the day at the country hospital. Walk and walk in the summer sun, but only manage four centimetres. Listen as another midwife says, 'I'm afraid we'll need to induce you.'

Arrive in the city hospital, to a room with five other women and no air con.

Then the real contractions begin. When they crescendo, you vomit all over yourself, pain like nothing you have felt before. 'Relax,' someone says, fixing you with fingers and now a monitor for the baby's heart. A man appears from nowhere, an angel in scrubs.

No time now for no worries. They heave you onto the trolley, hurtle down the hospital's identikit corridors. Try to sign your name as you scream. The needle scarcely has time to take effect before a voice says, 'We need to go in.'

The next thing you hear is a silence.

Then a cry. You wonder if it's yours.

After an eternity, the angel places your baby on your breast. 'Don't worry,' you hear yourself say. 'Mamma's here.'

Iso – From the Greek Meaning Equal – Usually Used as a Prefix, i.e. Isolation, Isobar, Isopod

Flynn

Flynn is in school 'iso', and Freya is gutted. They've been boyfriend and girlfriend for two weeks, and even though they have only hugged, she knows she's never met anyone like him. The other kids at school have already 'shipped' their names together. Like Kimye or Jelena, they are Freya + Flynn = Flya. She likes this. Imagines them taking flight together, escaping some of what makes life as a fourteen-year-old so eye-rollingly unfair. Her mum told her how she used to scratch the initials of the boys she liked into her pencil case with a compass, but Freya just thinks that's weird. She has an app that can merge a baby photo of her with one of Flynn to see what their kids might look like. She'd die of embarrassment if he knew that, though. Freya strokes her phone absent-mindedly, twists her hair and smiles into the screen, perfecting her pout before selecting the best filter. The teachers are punishing her too, not just the boy who will break her heart.

Jamie

Jamie has been tasked with planning a route that optimises the gradient and mileage for this Sunday's Strava cycle ride.

He and his mates call themselves the MAMILs: middle-aged men in Lycra. He's only forty-three, so objects slightly to the term middle-aged, though he knows he looks pretty good in the gear. Heather, one of the teaching assistants at school, told him so a few weeks ago after she'd seen him cycling past when she and her single friends were in the pub. Jamie hadn't noticed her before then, but he notices her every day now. Jamie flattens out the map, traces his fingers over the contours – imagines touching the contours of her. He recognises the symbols his father taught him, when he used to take him orienteering to give his mum some space. The isobars were always his favourite – the lines joining the same mean sea level air pressure. Jamie exhales and wonders where his father is now.

Helen

Helen dreams of being able to pee in peace. Or shower. Or finish a cup of tea. The kids have been yelling for her all day, and Jamie is busy obsessing about his bike, so she locks herself away in the bathroom, hoping nobody will find her here. She pours herself a bath, tips in some of the bottle of bubbles the kids bought her for Christmas, or Mother's Day, or her birthday – it doesn't really matter as the gifts are always the same. The water rises over her body, dousing the scar from Matty's emergency delivery, the small mound of her stomach, the pale breasts that still just about defy gravity after two bouts of breastfeeding. She closes her eyes, sinks into the water, inhales the heady perfume with its tropical fragrance. She pictures the last time she saw D, how his tongue touched every inch of her body like the water now. She remembers how they'd found each other at the prow of the boat, on the excursion put on by the conference organisers to show them the highlights beyond the hotel. She remembers D pointing at a crest of land rising off the Amalfi Coast, how he'd told her later that *isola* was Italian for island. She sinks beneath the bath's surface and blocks her ears to the shouting from downstairs, wondering what might have happened if she'd said yes to D and not no.

Matty

Matty is four. He can count to one hundred, forwards and backwards. He knows every number of every tank engine in Thomas, and the diesels. He knows what the world's biggest, smelliest plant is – the titan arum, before you ask. He knows that the Dead Sea is deep enough to hide the Eiffel Tower. He doesn't know what the Eiffel Tower is, but he does know that he loves *Spiderman* and *Batman* and *PAW Patrol* and the programme *Go Jetters*, where he laughs along with Ubercorn at his funky facts. Like Unicorns, Matty loves rainbows. He likes pink and purple, and he doesn't like monsters or mushrooms, crocodiles or sharks. Today he wishes he were a woodlouse. He watches one creep across the tiles in the toilet downstairs, wondering how a woodlouse poos. Matty thinks about poo a lot; it might even be his favourite word. He knows a woodlouse is an isopod. He does not know what iso means, but pod sounds a bit like poo, and he can spell both words.

How the Hostile Environment Instructor Failed to Teach Me About the Real Hostile Environment

Remember when we met, how you pointed your gun at me. 'If this wasn't an ambush, it would be phallic.' Muzzle in my hip, you clicked the safety catch, whispered: 'Don't worry, it's full of blanks.'

After the simulation, you bought me a drink, told me that now I knew the rules of war, I should realise some rules were meant to be broken.

We parted hours later; my eyes were red from drink, hands unsteady on my steering wheel. Before I reached the motorway, you texted me to meet you that weekend. In a Covent Garden camping store, we kissed, then you selected everything you said I'd need to stay safe: water-purifying tablets, mosquito net, first aid kit, tourniquet, penknife, DEET-impregnated clothes, a torch, a whistle.

The next day, I flew to my first frontline, filed to deadlines, and ignored the headlines. I watched as the world kept turning, blind to the reality of war.

Remember how you called me jetlagged and jaundiced, when I told you? You silenced me with a cup of tea stained with tannin and laughed when I admitted I had never watched porn. Under the Heathrow flight path, I heard your housemate phoning his girlfriend: his questions, her replies. I watched the contrails kiss in the sky, and when it was finally over, I showered in your filthy bathroom, fighting off the IKEA curtain sucking my skin.

You were hungry then. You took my hand along the Thames and told me about your ex. 'She had a body from *Baywatch*.' You drew hard on your cigarette, held your breath. I held mine. 'Then she got fucking pregnant, and I told her to get rid of it.' Like it was as simple as showering.

In the pub, you introduced me to your friends as a journalist, BBC, Oxford. Later, you said nobody wanted to listen to me go on about my achievements. Your regiment's insignia was inked in your skin. You'd forgotten to tell me you'd never been to war.

After Christmas, we went to the Alps with your mates. You'd all skied for the army. I felt like Bambi on the nursery slopes while you raced the black runs.

On New Year's Eve, we drank Jägerbombs and ate fondue, and the more you drank, the more you flirted with other women. Your mate crept closer as you moved further away.

'He handles his booze as badly as his birds,' he shouted over Auld Lang Syne before pulling you back for the fireworks.

Later, I held my breath while you both had your way with me, imagined trying to escape through the ice and darkness, not knowing where the crevasses cut the mountain in two. The next morning, I just wanted the virgin snow to swallow me whole.

You cried when I said we were finished. When you left, I didn't even look at the sky to see if your path kissed another, because I knew. And four weeks later, in another country, writing about another war, I knew again. Now there was a part of you no shower could wash away.

Remember what you said that first night about the gun being full of blanks? It's true that some rules are meant to be broken.

Before the Baby Was Born

Do you remember how you told me you'd drown our child if he were born with red hair like mine? You wanted a son, dark-crowned, a mirror of your own. You, who believed nothing that others told you, followed all the old wives' tales for this new wife of yours, who you only wed because in this new millennium, you did not want a bastard baby. Curries and walks and all the teas and tinctures that might bring on labour. And sex because didn't I know, you told me with all the coldness of a clinician eyeing his experiment, that semen ripened the cervix. It was in one of those fucking pub quizzes you hated that I finally let go to my body's natural rhythms, but only after I had proven to you that I knew more than you thought. If the contractions hadn't been so intense, we might have been first in the quiz, not second. Still, I believed another prize was mine: this child born ten days late, thirty hours after labour began, six hours after we made it to the hospital, twenty minutes after I wallowed into the water. A girl who defied the scan, with hair so black I only knew she was mine because of how she came to be. You took her away before I had given up the afterbirth, puffed up with the pride of your achievement and offered her a stay of execution, but not me. While I lay wasted but for the great clots I bled, you announced you were hungry and wanted to go home, but not before I took her from you, clamped her to my empty breast, a lion mother born.

A List of All the Places I've Loved and Lost You

Edinburgh

The statue of Greyfriars Bobby is just up the cobbles from my hotel. He died pining for his master. You pin me to the bed, and I wonder if this is what heaven feels like. In the morning, my tears taste like the salt of your lips after you licked me.

New York

The hotel is between Times Square and Broadway. Neon lights blink, and you whisper the lyrics of that Snow Patrol song. I loved you too before I even knew you. Off Times Square, our life comes full circle.

Athens

This is where I meet you, though I have met you many moons before. This is where our story becomes the myth, and we first ignore the fact we will be punished for our hubris.

Barcelona

You are bringing your new girlfriend here for the weekend, but until Friday comes, I will love you. You open the door to me, pour me Albariño and feed me albondigas, and when I taste you, I know I will never need to eat again.

Amsterdam

If I was smoking pot, perhaps there would be a reason for this feeling. Our lives are two parallel journeys: the world we inhabit and the world of us.

London

This is our city. The place we will always be. The Thames flows under Waterloo Bridge, and on the South Bank, I peer from the hotel window, watching how the water shifts but stays the same.

Sunday Best

I remember every Monday, the soft scent of soap, bubbles filling the air in your laundry room, clothes hanging from the line that Grandpa fixed from one wall to the other, the soft hum of the wireless. When the sun shone, I followed you outside, my feet in your footprints, toes pointed like yours. We danced beneath the clothes-line, spinning our way across the outdoor stage, hanging each item of clothing with an arabesque or grand jeté to our avian audience.

On Tuesdays after tea, I listened for the putt-putt of your old Citroën from streets away, then skipped from the house, curtseyed at your coming, snuggled into your blue cardigan, always blue, the same navy below-the-knee pencil skirt and row of pearls, for today's smell, cigarettes mingled with Pears soap and peppermints.

Wednesdays, I waited for the school bell to ring, practising my ballet positions under the table, then I ran across the playground, through the squealing throngs of other children, into your arms. On this Wednesday, you're there in your mid-week wear – a burgundy cardigan, grey skirt, white blouse fixed with an opal brooch, wearing a different smile – and as I lift my arms to yours, you perform a demi-plié, reach inside your bag, draw out a doll, my very own ballerina. We skip to your house, humming the tune from *Swan Lake*, my dolly dancing to the sweet sound of your memories, and I beg you to *tell me again about the time you danced with Margot Fonteyn?*

But Sunday is my favourite day. Sunday is when you invite me into your bedroom, where I sit at your polished mahogany dressing table and pick up the mother-of-pearl brush your mother gave you, that was her mother's, that you say will be mine one day. Sunday is when you untwist the plaits crowning your head, let me brush your waist-length hair, and suck Polo mints that make my nose all peppery, and whisper *don't tell Mummy and Daddy* when you light a cigarette to stop your coughing – and that makes the peppery feeling even worse – and we both collapse into fits of giggles when you say again *don't tell Mummy and Daddy*. Sunday is when you plait my hair, when you laugh as I walk, en pointe, on my tippy-toes, the Dabby walk, I still call it, even though I can say Granny now. Sunday is when you take my hand, and we walk to the kitchen, and you show me exactly how things were and how they always will be. I sit on the stool's faux leather seat, my Mary Jane shoe heels clicking against the metal bar, a captive audience as I fill my nostrils with a lifetime of memories, and you serve the roast beef and potatoes, then pass me the packaged Vienetta ice-cream with a curtsey, and I know when it comes to that final course, you won't tell Mummy and Daddy what we've already shared.

Lady Bugs

When Dexter talks, all the adults listen.

'Gee, he's so smart, our boy,' whispers May, just loud enough to make sure us kids will hear. He hovers by her side, all polished white teeth and retainer smile.

'Emily, why don't you take your cousin outside so you two can get some fresh air,' says Mum, nodding at her new nephew. I know there's no chance of me outrunning Dexter; I've already heard what an athlete he is.

'He was the youngest County Champion in his school's history,' says Uncle Frank, who's been calling himself Frankie since he went to America.

'The boy's on course for an athletics scholarship at college at this rate,' he bellows, his words louder and longer than they were before.

'Oh, Frankie, let's not get ahead of ourselves. Lots can happen in eight years,' says May. Her voice is high and squeaky like she's just breathed in a balloon, or the hot air that Dad says comes out of Uncle Frankie's mouth.

'Lots can happen in eight months,' is what I want to say, but I know better than to be cheeky to my new auntie and her darling Dexter. Uncle Frankie is staring like he's never seen anyone like them. I try to see what he sees. May is pretty in a beauty pageant way. Big hair, boobs almost as big, short skirt and the whitest teeth I have ever seen. Dexter has the coolest pair of Nike trainers and a shirt buttoned up to his neck that makes him look quite handsome, even if it's a bit posh for this occasion. Minus the train tracks on his teeth, he has a mouth like his mum's, wide and white, and I look at him wishing my smile was like that. If the adults all love him, he can't be that bad, surely? Maybe I am just jealous. I mean, I know it's nice to finally have a cousin my age and one who lives in somewhere as cool as Florida, of all places. And even if he doesn't seem to want to play with me right now, he did at least give me that NASA baseball cap and the pack of freeze-dried ice cream just like astronauts eat.

I hear Mum say something about 'love at first sight', and Frankie nods, and I try to feel happy for my uncle and my mum who almost exploded with excitement when Frank FaceTimed her to say he'd got married to a woman he'd met online eight months ago, and he was bringing her and her son home to meet the family, and by the way, he'd adopted the son who was just the coolest kid, and he was sure that he and I would just hit it off.

I stand still at the bottom of the steps to the garden, watching Dexter grow taller with every nice thing they say about him. I wish they would say something nice about me too.

When I run, my face goes beetroot, and I get all out of breath, but I know all my times tables, and I've read all of the Harry Potter books. I want my mum to say something about how well I'm doing, about how I want to be an astronaut when I grow up, about how she reckons I could be the first woman on Mars. But all I can hear is Dexter this and Dexter that. I want to ask Dexter what he likes to play, but he seems quite happy just as he is.

A ladybird lands on my arm, and I turn my head to count its spots. Its red is the exact same shade as the dress I chose to wear in honour of my new family. I raise my finger to my mouth and motion for Dexter to creep closer, wanting to show him this tiny, fragile creature and ask him if they have them in Florida too. Dexter lunges towards me, snatches the insect and flicks it onto its back: black instead of red. He tears off a leg, laughs, moves towards me and lowers his voice.

'Back home, we call them ladybugs. Bugs are meant to be crushed.' The adults smile, but I know they don't hear.

Jesus to a Child

Today my four-year-old found the Lord in his lunchbox. Tucked between the apple slices and the yoghurt tubes, Charlie might have missed the miracle, but fortunately for him and the future of faith, his form teacher Miss Angel was on hand.

I had feared as much ever since I saw the letters C of E carved into the wooden board beneath the school name, and even more since the heavenly faced young woman pulled me and Ryan to one side, as if we were the chosen ones.

'You must be Charlie's parents?' she said, her painted eyebrows tiny slugs on her otherwise perfect face. I nodded, feeling the murmurings of approval from my husband, and stretched out my hand, trying not to compare her rosy pink shellac nails with my nibbled nudes.

'I'm just not sure about this place,' I told Ryan, as we walked home after that open evening, reversing the route Charlie and I would take for the next seven years.

'Oh, Janey, you need to let go of the past. This one's not Catholic, like your school, and anyway, I thought you wanted to give our boy a head start?' He smiled, and I pictured him imagining the staff room's hottest new pin-up, halo over her head, wings sprouting from her tanned shoulders.

'I do,' I said, seeing our longed-for baby until his image became a blur of memories. 'I do,' I murmured, remembering the nights I spent waking from dreams where the nuns hauled Hail Marys from my mouth, and the days treading on eggshells, shielding my soft skin from the cane as they threatened hell and damnation for my mortal sins.

I should have told Ryan then and there that lust was also a mortal sin, and perhaps Miss Angel was one of the fallen kind, but I let it go.

And now Charlie is coming to the end of his first term, and all that's left is the festivities – the Christmas fayre, Santa's grotto, the nativity. I never made it past the third shepherd for my stage performances. Ryan failed to graduate from the farmyard. But I have big hopes for my boy.

With his dad away at work, Charlie and I cuddle in bed. He's all cherubic blonde curls and puppy fat. In his *PAW Patrol* pyjamas, he seems more like a baby than a schoolboy. He's just finished his warm milk and looks up earnestly, a cream moustache lining his lips.

'Mumma,' he says, 'Miss Angel says because I been such a good boy, I get to play with cheeses.' I look at him, wondering how in all those years of hearing the Christmas story, I missed the fact it took place in a dairy, not a stable. 'What was that, my cherub?' I ask. 'Miss Angel said I could play with the cheeses. But I told her, Mummy doesn't let me play with my food, and anyway, I like jam, not Jesus in my sandwich.'

Jugo Especial

In Lima's central market, next to the rows of plastic dolls with peroxide hair, above the neon dogs that jump and bark when the stallholders clap, there's a stand stacked high with glass jars. Beneath them, cardboard signs read *jugo especial*. Special juice. I know why it's special but figure your Spanish doesn't stretch as far as understanding the subtext.

Each is filled with a bright liquid, the same shade as the spinach and kale, courgette and watercress juices, accompanied by inflated promises and prices back home. You're already a convert to these other wonder drinks, but you never managed to convince me.

'It tastes like dirt,' I scowled when you offered me a taste of your tonics, but you kept buying this shit rather than my excuses.

'Does it really matter, if it has the required effect?' you said, and I watched the space between us grow as you became smaller and smaller.

When I got my job posting to Peru, you promised to visit. Your private school teaching gave you long holidays. You'd come and stay. We'd find a way to make things work from a distance. Life was cheap here. I could earn enough for the two of us, and we'd still have time and money to see this exotic country. I imagined us like explorers discovering the new world. 'We might even rediscover each other,' I ventured.

'It's no good, Tim,' you said, your voice croaking, and I wondered if it was you or the crap connection. 'I think we should just be friends. It's just not fair on either of us.' I knew you were trying to be kind. I'd seen how your eyes shone when you mentioned your maths colleague Miles. In the past, I might have made a wisecrack about a name that would go the distance, but I didn't.

You were still committed to coming, of course. You'd bought the cheapest flight, no refund available, and so I didn't bother changing my plans.

We'd hike the Inca Trail, visit Machu Picchu, see the condors soar on the thermals above the Colca Canyon. I'd take you to the jungle, show you sloths and caimans, all the animals that were unique to this part of the world. I didn't tell you how some of these exotic creatures were known to possess supernatural qualities. I didn't tell you I still loved you and would do anything to win you back.

'Promise me, there'll be no funny business,' you said, pecking me on the cheek at the airport, surrounded by Peruvians embracing their loved ones like they'd been separated forever.

'I promise,' I said. 'But in return, promise me you'll be open to all Peru has to offer.' You nod, a nervous glance at the crowd before us.

And so, we're at the market, and I'm playing tour guide. You point to the jars, and your smile widens for the first time in days. Your Spanish is basic, but you recognise that *jugo* is juice, and *especial* doesn't need a big mental leap.

But my mind is elsewhere. I'm thinking about the interview I did with the radio station back in the UK, talking about the illegal trade in Amazonian frogs known for their aphrodisiac qualities, which had been tracked down to a market in the capital. After the interview ended, the presenter asked me if I'd tried any yet, and I had to admit I hadn't, but now you're here – it would seem remiss not to try the local delicacy. And knowing your penchant for pure living and the promised effects of the juice, I'm sure you'll be up for it sooner rather than later.

I hand over my payment, and the stallholder passes you the two jars. He winks at me, and by the time I wink back, you're already half-finished, and I wonder how long it will be until we can start again.

The Thin Line Between Everything and Nothing

i) *She's Every Woman*

The snow is window high, and we are cocooned. Upstairs your mother moves across the kitchen with the religious precision of a Martha Stewart disciple. You turn up the music. Remember how I laughed when I first heard this song? Today it becomes our anthem. 'Garth Brooks sure hasn't met you,' you say. 'You're not every woman. You're the only woman.'

ii) *Cockroaches*

Even the cockroach knows the door is stuck. I tug the handle, shove my shoulder into the wood so hard I'm sure it will leave a forever mark. It doesn't budge. I fall back against the wall, hear the cockroach scuttle into the corner, and the sound of its freedom pops like gunfire from the grey peeling walls.

iii) *The Man with the Hammer*

The man is outside of his car before we even register you have cut him up. He's wielding a hammer and a can of lager like it's perfectly usual to carry both in a car. He weapons his words too – and I'm starting to hear them above the heating and closed windows and the radio to warn us of accidents or roadworks, or any of the other irritants of a normal Thursday morning that might today mean the difference between everything and nothing.

iv) Fire and Ice

Your kisses on my flat belly are snowflakes on my skin. Garth Brooks is singing about fire and ice, and I am melting in your arms, beneath your tongue. When the song darkens, and this man describes his every woman 'raging like a river', you laugh. 'I can't imagine you ever being like that,' you say. 'Then you don't know me,' I think, naked in front of you. In two months' time, it'll be you raging on the edge of the Snake River Canyon.

v) The Smell of Fear

The toilet bowl is full, and I inhale the fear of more than just me. The fear of everyone else who has been here since the world shook and seconds became the difference between life and death. The cockroach has escaped under the door, and I watch as the shit slips from side to side and I slide to the floor.

vi) Judgement Day

Judges don't take kindly to defendants being late, and if I'm to stand any chance of getting her back, we need to be on time. I can hear the man's words. He's every man. With his hammer, he yells; 'I'm gonna fucking bray you.' Your hand is on the door, ready to shield me again. 'No, Dad, please,' I beg. 'Let me.' I open it slowly, the way I was taught to approach a checkpoint in war. My legs shake like they will later when I beg the judge to let me see my child. Like they did when I stood at her father's door, asking for the same.

A Linguistic Theory of Bats

We are in the college bar, drinking snakebite and black, you watching another match on TV, jumping and jeering like it's a matter of life or death. I'm trying to tell you my theory about the word for *bat* in different European languages, and you think I'm talking about something to do with the game that has gone on all day, and I say not cricket bat: I'm talking about the flying kind, and I reckon the words we use for these animals say something about our cultures. So, for instance, the French word is *chauve-souris* which translates as *bald mouse*, but before I can explain what this says about Gallic sensibilities, you say it's my turn to buy a round and anyway, you can't concentrate with me rabbiting on. So, I leave you with the Italian *pipistrelle*, which is more romantic than its root word *vesper*, as in *night*, not Vespa as in I wish I could ride off into the sunset with someone who listens and loves me. And I head for the bar, thinking of the German *fledermaus*, or *flying mouse*, and how I should just take a leaf from this literal language and tell you we are *kaput*, when someone brushes my arm and says something which sounds like you could do better. He speaks so softly I have to lean in to listen, and I figure he looks and sounds Latino, so I ask him if he knows what bat is in Spanish and flap my arms just in case. He smiles, all teeth, and I imagine him sucking my blood, bringing me back to life. He mouths *mur-c-i-e-l-a-go*. It's the only Spanish word with every vowel, I say. And I know the fact it means *blind mouse* doesn't matter, because I can finally see.

Birthday Girl

It's Anna's tenth birthday. She wakes to the sound of nothing, slips her feet from the bottom bunk, careful not to stand on the empty wrappers scattered across the floor by Joey. He's her dad's housemate and sleeps here when Anna doesn't. It's bad enough that he leaves his clothes in a spare drawer next to hers and that she found a pack of cigarette filters slipped between her two Harry Potter books, which were her mum's first editions and really should be back at the other house. But Anna knows she can't say anything to Daddy about the fact she doesn't like having some unrelated teenager sleeping in her bed, because he's already told her he needs someone else living there so he can afford the rent, and, anyway, if her mum saw sense and let Anna live with him full time, it would be different, and she would get her own room, all the time.

On nights when Anna lives with her dad, he sleeps on the sofa, and Joey gets her dad's bedroom, sometimes by himself and sometimes with one of the girls he brings back from the pub where Anna went once with the two of them, where Joey bought her a coke, and she got a free refill, and her dad told her not to tell her mum cos she wouldn't get it, any of it, and Anna sat and read the whole of *The Philosopher's Stone* while the men drank beer.

Anna knows she should be grateful for the fact Joey gives her dad money and that her dad lets Joey sleep in his bed when she's there because otherwise she'd be on the bottom bunk with Joey on the top.

Anna's dad says he's got a special ability to sleep anywhere – a trick from his army days – but sometimes it takes him a bit to get to sleep, and sometimes she worries about how long because she's heard him late at night, thrashing and crashing in the living room with the TV up high, and she can smell the smoke creeping up the stairs, and she wishes it was him coming to give her a hug, not the stink of his cigarettes wrapping their ashy arms around her.

Anna has learned to be very quiet. She can get herself up and dressed, sort her breakfast, make Dad a cup of tea, nice and strong like back in the army, and today, because it's her birthday, he's said she can walk to school all by herself. Mum says she wouldn't dream of letting Anna walk alone, but that's because she's over-protective and still treats Anna like a baby – at least that's what Dad says.

Anna dresses silently, passes the door to her dad's room where Joey is still asleep, and she creeps down the stairs, trying not to get her hopes up about the present promises her dad made, knowing that it's not his fault he can't get her much right now, but wondering if he did remember which of the Harry Potter books was next on her list.

There are no presents downstairs, nothing wrapped on the living room table like there would be at Mum's, no loud welcome from her baby brother, or awful singing from her stepdad, no phone in her face as her mum tries to record the first moment when she sees her daughter in double digits.

Instead of presents, the living room is covered with empty cans, one knocked over and spilt across the table, and there's a puddle on the carpet where it has dripped over the edge, and Anna can hear the landlady already – telling her dad he's over-stayed his welcome and she's only not kicked them out cos he has a kid – and it's not her fault he's a mental case, and that she's not a bloody charity case. And she wonders if the land-lady knows about Joey, and she thinks probably not.

Anna empties the ashtray but knows she won't be able to clean her hands of the smell. Then she picks up the cans and puts them by the recycling box in the garage because it's al-ready full and the bottles don't get collected for another three weeks.

And she creeps back inside and opens the cupboard where the cereals are kept and measures a handful of Cheerios into a chipped bowl, and closes her eyes, making a wish – because it is her birthday after all – and she wishes eating them might make her feel like the name – cheery-oh. And then she feels greedy for wishing something so selfish. And she wonders how you can feel greedy and hungry at the same time?

The milk smells bad, so she eats the little circles of cereal dry, studying each carefully, trying not to eat them too fast because the box has to last until next payday, which is even further away than the next bottle collection.

The milk means she can't make her dad a cup of tea, so she doesn't dare bother him, and even if she did, he looks quite peaceful lying on the sofa in the same clothes he wore yester-day.

Tonight, he'll take her to Tesco as a treat, and they'll get a pizza from the reduced section and pay for it in pennies.

When Anna goes back to her mum's tomorrow, she'll get asked what her dad got for her birthday, with that look that says just how much Mum hates him. Anna will tell her Daddy is going to get a dog, but she won't say he's waiting till he's back on his feet, and she won't mention that the dog makes her think about what her dad said when her mum got pregnant. That she was only having the baby in case Anna died, and if she did, her dad would get a dog. Instead, Anna will bite into the cake her stepfather baked, and she'll taste the tobacco on her fingertips.

Drosophila melanogaster

The fruit fly shares the same genes as a human. Its Latin name is *Drosophila melanogaster*, which sounds awfully fancy for something attracted to rotten fruit and vegetables. I think about the time you told me I smelt ripe when you forced me onto my back in that room with the torn sheets. Fruit flies breed in drains, empty bottles and waste disposals, relying on a moist layer of material that ferments to grow their families. The adults have brown trunks, black bottoms and crimson eyes and are so small they can creep through windows and doors that aren't properly covered. I think about the time we met, how I was bruised and broken, how you flew to my side, hovered around me, your tanned arms winged in a false promise. The reproductive potential of a fruit fly is enormous, and given the chance, they can lay five hundred eggs. Your first girlfriend had an abortion; you left your second after you boasted how easy it would be for you to get her pregnant. You tell me this as you lie, limp and damp, and I see your eyes turn red with tears. Soon you're snoring. You don't hear me creep away to mop up the smell of me or move to the window above the bins, where I watch their bags spilling into the car park. Your snores sound like the buzz of five hundred flies surfacing from the fetid food when I leave you in your waste.

No Place for a Girl

'This is no place for a girl.' His warning collided with the crowd's chants. Eva had tried to hide her sex beneath the armour of media masculinity. Boots, combats, a duty-free shirt to cover her bum. Beneath it, her swimsuit stuck to her skin.

Jemma had suggested the swimsuit. They were the only women on the hostile environments course, taught by a former special-forces bloke, whose way with women had not improved despite three marriages.

At night, the men verbally masturbated over stories they daren't share at home. The babies who lay on their haunches in death, like their own toddlers slept at night; the pear-drop smell of putrefying corpses.

Later, loose-lipped from lager, they flirted with Jemma and Eva. 'Our other halves don't get us; only you know what it's like.'

~

Eva planned to stick to the edge of the crowd and duck in for a few quotes and general shots. Her phone buzzed deep in her pocket.

'Still no visa. There asap.' She'd wait for Oli here. Her swimsuit was icy Lycra. She shuddered, checked the signs: Saeed Street. Outside KFC.

'No worries.' She hit send, firing reassurances as the sky split. She ducked with the memory of muscles taut and taught.

The crowd surged back. Behind her, glass splintered, and metal groaned, dismembered from its chain. Colonel Sanders slumped to the street.

A hand pulled her up. '*Shukran.*' The next hand wasn't helping but hurting.

'No,' she shouted before her mouth was masked with metal, blood, grit.

'No.' In that vacuum, words vanished. Not English, not Arabic. Nothing.

By Colonel Sanders, her camera's red light blinked. Its lens focussed on a crushed carton of drumsticks, flesh ripped from bone, and a tub of exploded ketchup – blood-red sauce.

The Toy

The toy wears a blue plastic coat and white peaked cap. Its legs were once white too, but now one is red, the clumsy crayoning of a toddler.

I pull it from my pocket, press it in my hand, unyielding. But then it crumples in the middle. And I fold too, remembering when I last wore this coat.

We were at the café last week, a bleak January morning, warming ourselves after swimming. Freya had other toys at home, planes and ambulances, for hours of fun. But there, she quickly tired of the lone figure and scribbled on its leg with a Crayola pulled from the back of the crumbed sofa. She howled when I thrust the toy in my pocket, binned the crayon with the wasted cups.

And now here it is with me in another world. I wish I hadn't held on to it. Because in future, whenever I pick up a Playmobil, I'll be back in this country of stolen childhood.

It was a tissue I had been searching for to give the little girl. She's not much older than Freya, her leg the same blood red as the toy. 'Oh, oh,' she whispers, then, 'Mama, Mama.' Of course, *eau* is French for water. But *Mama* stays the same. I can't comfort her loss or her love.

I take the tissue and a bottle of water from my bag. But I cannot magic her mother. I grip the Playmobil person and sense my own daughter there.

The Species of Pangolin Compromise Their Own Order: Pholidota

Pholi – A folly is something stupid.

Dota – She's learning phonics at school. This is how she would spell *daughter*.

He said I was *fucking stupid*. Ordered me to get rid of it. I cradled my belly's soft shell as it grew.

'Pangolin' comes from the Malay 'pengguling', *loosely meaning something that rolls up.*

Later, I stuffed into a rucksack all we needed to survive, hiding our future beneath my bed. I curled up by her cot.

Special glands near the pangolin's anus secrete a pungent fluid as a defence mechanism.

Now the court toilet smells of the fear of losing my child.

That last night, he came home drunk. I'd not showered for two days between the feeding, burping, changing, rocking, cooking. He hissed at me when I begged him to be quiet.

You smell ripe. He tore at my clothes. *Why can't you make a fucking effort?* Pinned me to the bed. Cried when he came. Then she cried too. By the time I had settled her, he was snoring. The room reeked of shame.

Pangolins are nocturnal animals. Their shells made of keratin, the same substance as human hair and nails.

In the shower, I scrubbed myself raw, let the water sear my scalp. Impossible to feel clean.

The mother curls up around the baby pangolin if she senses danger.

He left for work. Then we left. I clasped her to me, promising he would not hurt us again.

Now I hear my name, calling me to court.

The endangered pangolin is the world's most trafficked animal; its body parts are sold as a delicacy or used for their mythical healing properties.

When my daughter is older, I will teach her how to protect herself. One day, I will explain what being endangered really means.

It's a Jungle out There

He offers me a coffee. Decaf Nescafé out of a sachet. UHT milk, which dribbles from the tiny pot as he peels off the plastic lid. The hot drink burns my tongue. He slips off his boat shoes, drops his jeans on the IKEA carpet. Together we tear off the clothes I had ordered especially; my tight trousers peel off like a snake shedding its skin, my expensive jumper crumples to the floor. I breathe in, still in the underwear that cost me a week's salary. It's been a long time since I felt this naked. Without his clothes, he's paler, podgier than I imagined. But if he's embarrassed, he doesn't show it. Flecks of white hair sprout from his nipples. A caiman's tooth hangs from his neck.

'It's from the time I trekked the Amazon,' he told me earlier as I reached towards him, touching the place where it hung between the buttons of his checked shirt. He took it off, showed me the tiny beads that made up the necklace. 'These are *huayruro* seeds. The locals swear by them for fortune and fertility.' He winked. 'I've worn it on every expedition since.' Then he pressed the sharp end of the tooth gently to the pad of my pinkie, and I felt the stab of something other than pain.

Now I watch him moving over me, remember how he said that conquest was more about the mind than the body. With every move he makes, the caiman tooth swings like a hypnotist's charm.

Afterwards, I pop the lid on the shower gel, allow the liquid to spill over me. I breathe in its false promise, the factory fragrance supposed to capture the rainforest. I turn up the heat and step out of the shower. My skin is red raw and smells of disappointment.

How Do You Classify Mammals?

At first, Dom seemed okay about selling the Z3. We posted it on *Auto Trader* then spent hours poring over *Which Car?* weighing up family-friendly designs. We had already sold the flat and bought a four-bed house with a garage, now home to a BabyJogger buggy. I had no intention of holding on to the baby weight after the birth.

Dom seemed to be wobbling. Halfway through building the spreadsheet to compare the cars, he took the final chocolate Hobnob. Lying on the sofa, our distended bellies balancing the Mac, I laughed, 'If I'm eating for two, you must be eating for three.'

'I won't be late. Just meeting the lads for a quick half,' he messaged after work the next day. I texted him the photo from the twenty-week scan: 'It's okay if you tell them the sex.'

I calculated how long a half-pint would take with Tom and John, and multiplied it by three, just in case they all chipped in to celebrate. Then I added fifteen minutes because beer goes straight through Dom, especially since he turned forty. He hadn't taken kindly to me telling him older men often experienced enlarged prostates and that he would be bound to wee more.

After an hour, I googled 'mindfulness' on YouTube. After two hours, I gave up and walked to the Forresters. The first thing I saw as I turned the corner to our local was a group of men, all of them dressed in Lycra, each glued to a gleaming bike.

I remember Dom reading an article in *The Observer* about this breed of 'MAMILs', or middle-aged men in Lycra.

I laughed as he told me that a MAMIL's head was usually hidden under a hard, helmet-like shell to protect his receding hairline, his expanding girth cinched by tight Lycra, and the rest of his body swaddled to leave little to the imagination.

From the accompanying photos and text, I saw a MAMIL wore his manhood with pride, straddled his bike as if he'd never had a ride like it, and terrorised members of the opposite sex with talk of tight clothes, time trials and titanium frames.

I scoffed at the play on words with mammal as if these imposters could possibly have anything in common with warm-blooded animals whose females fed their infants milk through mammary glands.

'Jesus, Amanda, if I ever turn into one of them, you have my permission to pull down my cycling shorts and publicly flog me,' Dom had said to me over a glass of Malbec. It was the last day of our honeymoon, and we'd got so drunk that my pill had failed.

Touching my ballooning boobs, I fought back my envy of these men. My phone vibrated in my bag. Dom must be home.

'Amanda, is that you?' I heard his voice before I recognised him, lifted my eyes to the gleaming bike, the helmeted creature in front of me, his enlarged prostate pulsing inside his lurid Lycra.

Birth Plan

A birth plan records what you would like to happen during your labour and after the birth. You can change your mind about these wishes at any time.

Your name: You will answer to your given name until you give birth. From then on, you will be Mum or a variant of, or any other title in accordance with the loss of your identity.

Due date: Relatively random date chosen by medical person which becomes watershed moment between old and new life and is only correct four per cent of the time and may be wrong by two weeks leading to frenzied attempts to induce labour, including but not limited to curry, pineapple, extra sex (which is a last resort given how totally impractical it is to hump a hippo).

Where to give birth: You may imagine giving birth in a pool, with relaxing music, fragrant oils. In truth, you will not give a shit where you give birth after forty hours of labour. Correction: you will give a shit (of the faeces variety), which prior to this moment would have freaked you out, but you won't metaphorically give a shit about anything other than pushing the equivalent of a pineapple out of your nostril.

Your birth partner or companion: Husband. Later to be known as bastard, why the fuck did you do this? I hate you, hold my hand, don't hold my hand, go away, oh shit, oh shit, and finally, Daddy.

Monitoring during labour: Your midwife will have discussed with you how you would like your baby's heart to be monitored if everything is straightforward.

Your comments on monitoring your baby during labour: The moment when the doctor shoves his fingers up your vagina to attach a monitor to the baby's head, and the machine shows his heart rate falling is the moment you know this is no longer straightforward.

Skin-to-skin contact with your baby: After the birth, your baby can be placed onto you before the cord is cut. You may prefer to ask the midwife to wipe and wrap your baby in a blanket first.

Your comments on anything special you would like to happen immediately after the birth: You don't care and will just want to hold that tiny blood-and-fluid-smeared thing, and you will want to keep on holding it for ever and ever.

Your preferences for pain relief: Any idea you had of natural pain relief you reject within three hours. Gas and air make you vomit. By the time you ask for an epidural, it's too late. By the time it's too late, the anaesthetist can only wait for the numbing to reach beneath your nipples before the surgeon goes in.

But when you hold your baby, the pain goes away, and you realise what a drug true love is. (At least until the anaesthetic wears off, and your wound gets infected and your milk comes in.)

Faithful Friend

In dog years, we have known each other a lifetime. In human years, it's scarcely long enough for us to notice the shift in each other's bodies, the sag and expanse of our own, the strips of grey and white in our hair, the extra lines around our eyes.

You are the same to me now as when we met on the edge of Edinburgh's oldest graveyard.

'Do you know this is supposed to be the city's most haunted place?' you asked me.

'That's a chat-up line if ever I heard one,' I answered with the cockiness of someone newly married.

'I was kidding. I guess this is the reason you're here.' You pointed at the statue of Greyfriars Bobby, and I nodded. I didn't tell you I had been walking these streets all week, killing time while my husband was at some work thing.

'A bonnie wee chap, don't you think?' Your hair was as dark as the metal from which the statue was made. Something about the way you spoke made me wonder if you were right, that perhaps this place really was haunted.

'Do you know the story?'

I paused, shook my head. I did but wanted to hear it from you.

'You've not heard anything yet.' You blew your heavy fringe from your eyes, and perhaps it was a trick of the light in this magical place, but I could have sworn you winked.

It becomes our mantra, even though we hear everything from each other, even though we come to know each other almost as well as we know ourselves. 'You've not heard anything yet', we write by text, or we whisper in those precious moments when we come together. 'You've not heard anything yet' becomes our code to say the coast is clear and we can escape our adopted lives – the existences we fall into despite each other: my unhappy marriage, your divorce.

Once a year, we meet here, by the statue of the Skye Terrier. To the world, we could be two strangers speaking for the first time.

'You must have heard the tale of Bobby?' you say, my signal to shake my head like I did back then, because even though I've always known the tale of the faithful dog, each time I hear it, I'm reminded what loyalty really means.

And so you tell me in your Scottish brogue, the story of the wee terrier, of his faithfulness to his master, of how after his owner's death, he refused to leave his grave at Greyfriars Kirk.

I watch as you weave the story of a loyalty so strong it outlived all attempts to adopt the animal. I watch as you watch me, noticing the way you squint when you're at your most serious, the same way you did that first time when I thought you were winking at me. Your hair has receded now, and you no longer have the same fringe as when we first met, so instead, you blow me a kiss when we finally dare to say goodbye.

Neither of us ever broaches what will happen when we can no longer meet here.

Love Is Many Things,
None of Them Logical*

1. As You Wish*

It's been snowing for days. School has been cancelled, and I want to go outside to make a snow angel. 'It'll be the death of you,' my host mother, Mary-Lou, warns me, turning the TV on to *The Princess Bride* for the fifth time in five days. Mary-Lou doesn't know that I lost my virginity on Valentine's Day last week. I doubt she really understands what it's like to be in love, even though she's had six children. 'Life isn't fair, it's just fairer than death, that's all,' I whisper. Buttercup and Westley get it.

2. Inconceivable*

I'm drinking a tiny coffee in a corner café by the cobbled edge of the water in Rovinj, watching the boats bob in the blue Adriatic and planning the next stage of my solo backpacking trip. There's a television above the bar that only the owner seems to be interested in. It fizzes with black-and-white images and a language I don't understand. I don't know why my eyes shift to the screen, but in that split second, I watch a plane fly into a tower and hear the words 'holy fuck' from somewhere. I book the next boat to Venice, not knowing if I'll

ever get there for my honeymoon now, and certainly not prepared to wait.

3. This is true love. Do you think this happens every day?*

The man has his back turned to me, but even before I see his
face, I know I'm in love with him. He has his right hand firmly
inside the carcass of a bird, though I can't tell from this distance if it's a chicken or turkey. His blonde curls bob with
concentration, and his left foot rises and falls, keeping rhythm
with some music I can't yet hear, but I already know will form
the soundtrack to our future.

4. Since the invention of the kiss*

Your mouth is on mine, and you are kissing me like you have
not eaten for one hundred days. Your lips taste like liquorice,
and my mouth melts into yours. Together we devour the bowl
of Ben & Jerry's ice cream, and then you scrape the bottom of
the tub and smear it over my flat stomach. When you lick it off,
you linger a little longer, spinning circles with your tongue on
my tummy. You look up at me, your eyes sated, and you say, 'If
it's twins, let's call them Cookies and Cream.'

5. You fell victim to one of the classic blunders*

Cochabamba is jungle hot. The sweat slips down my back behind my thin shirt and pools in my pants. The lights of the
hotel fizz and burn, and my belly aches from the Bolivian
street food I bought, even though I knew from the very first
bite, I would regret it. I climb onto the hotel treadmill, deter-
mined to run even though my brain and body say no. Turn up
the speed, worry about a power cut, watch as the numbers get
higher and higher, listen to the beating of my feet like drums
that carry me away. I stop counting, fall back off the machine,

into the cool concrete wall. In three days' time, I'll know it wasn't the food.

6. We'll never survive. Nonsense, you're only saying that because no one ever has*

The militia march past, a ragged battalion of men in borrowed fatigues, and we are squeezed beneath the table in the house, our hosts sitting towards the front of the blown-out window. Sarah wears the only Kevlar helmet in our group of journalists, and I'm half under the wood, half out, when the roof starts to shake. I see a trickle become a torrent, and I scream my children's names, but the only thing that falls from my mouth is dust.

---

*The Princess Bride. Dir. Rob Reiner. 20th Century Fox, 1987.

La Cucaracha

The Cucaracha is one of the most basic moves in Latin dancing, but when I watch you demonstrate it, I realise that sometimes the simplest things are the most stunning. You slide your toes to the side, shift your weight back to your first foot and then snap your legs together. I am mesmerised by you. I've seen you dancing each evening on the terrace overlooking the Malecon, the Caribbean backdrop shifting with the rhythm of your body. It's as if you control the pull of the tides as well.

For the first time this week, when you pause, you turn to me and smile. I am drawn by the tightness of your lips, the perfect outline of you. I follow you towards the makeshift bar, the wooden walls stacked high with bottles of clear spirits. The only one I recognise is Bacardi. I know that this was the place where it was first distilled.

'Can I get you a drink?' I stammer in my best Spanish.

'If you let me teach you,' you nod. Your English is almost perfect, accented so lightly some might struggle to notice. My smile when you answer makes me wonder only briefly about the amount of rum in this mojito.

'La Cucaracha, it's also a folk song,' you say after I buy the second round. Now your palms graze my outer thighs as you guide me to make moves that I never thought this middle-aged body could.

'Tell me what it's about,' I ask, losing myself in the way you separate each syllable just like you separate each step.

'It means many things, but it's mainly associated with revolutions.' My stomach flips, and you pull me closer.

When you kiss me later, I taste the rum on your lips. Later still, your hands will touch every part of my body, and your words will crack the hard shell I have worn for years.

When I wake the next morning, you have gone; so too has the purse that fell to the floor as you stripped me of my clothes. I hold onto the word as I turn on my phone, speak its slow syllables out loud. I learn cucaracha means cockroach. It turns out they are hard to catch and even harder to crush.

Hooked

Waiters rove between our tables, unthreading meat from metal skewers, slipping them onto slabs, juices seeping. They weave between the churrascaria and the Samba dancers like practised partners, a choreography that cold-shoulders the women.

All the other customers of this restaurant are from Rio: *Cariocas* – unflustered by the taut, tanned limbs, the flicks and kicks.

Not me.

I am mesmerised by these dancers in their turquoise thongs, sequined tassels spouting from their breasts, feathers sprouting from their flesh. They drip theatrical desire like the sauce spreading across my plate from the steak – both prepared *à point*.

Faster and faster, they flap and flutter, and as the music crescendos, they soar. Then the sound fades, and with the falling rhythm, they retreat from their feathers; just flesh.

I want to hide too, but João says I'm not safe alone in his city.

Silent chains bind me to him beneath the buzz and chatter, and I watch him with his friends who come and go – who ooze privilege – who sink beef and booze. I tell myself, don't sink just yet, hold on, as they think of nothing but their next Carménère, their next *rodízio* rump.

Uncalled, ignored, the dancers deliver their encore. I try to catch their gaze, but their sights are somewhere else, and they slip into the shadows.

I am out of my depth.

João catches my eye, nudges his friend Frederico whose stare is dull as day-old fish, not the snook speared from the waters around Rio. His lips open and close. His words drown.

Now the dancers have fled to their favelas; the rich residents retired to Copacabana, Zona Sul, Leblon. Lives blend in the leftovers, wine spilt, claret against cream cloth, empty bottles skittle-like, waiting to fall, a single feather, jungle green.

Frederico turns, eyes grey glass, mouth flaccid.

'You like the meat?'

'Si,' I say, years of yes instead of no.

In the taxi, the men's foreign words wash over me, too fast for me to grasp, but their stares linger. João watches through the rear-view mirror, Frederico from alongside.

We cruise up to a compound, gates reel us in.

João's apartment is a goldfish bowl; glass, and light, bright.

My head is swimming.

I circle around and around.

Inside.

Inside.

I am hooked.

To thrash would be to make it worse. No is the same in both our worlds, and underwater.

Set Directions

Like a dolls' house posed before playtime, a stage set before the first act. The furniture perfectly positioned, not a chair out of place. Sunday's finest tablecloth laid with dishes lovingly prepared, all of them in miniature.

But wait. The audience is here: the woman who was once the little girl who rearranged the figures around the furniture, playing God over the little people.

Now she stands outside the home where she might have lived had destiny's dice rolled another number.

Now she peers at a safe distance onto the scene, remembering how she had sworn she would come back to tell their story: this journalist who forgot about her promise to them.

She is the little girl who abandoned her plaything, who let the dust settle on the dolls and the tiny trinkets tumble to the floor; the young woman who stumbles to the loft one day, long after she has packed up her promise in the same yellowed paper; the woman who tried to find truth in fiction rather than fact, who fails to remember where the two converge.

Now, she stands on the fault lines of her future and wonders what has happened to the fabric of her past.

The Muse

The artist bids me put on the robe and sit here: still.

'Take the book in your hands. Make pretence you are reading.'

When I was a young girl, Father would sit me on his knee, tell me tales of far-off lands. When he returned from his travels, he would gift me books, and I would beg him to take me to the worlds contained therein. He told me reading held the key for girls like me. Because I was not a boy. Because there had been a boy who had not survived and a mother who had not survived either, he taught me like a son. But I was not a son.

One day, he called me to him.

'I must go away. But when I return, I will bring you a whole universe of books and together we will escape this world.'

But he never returned. His ship sank, and with it, the page slammed shut.

And because he did not teach me to be like a daughter, I did not know how to be around respectable men after.

Now the artist bids me dress, make pretence. He does not know my father taught me many things, but he never taught me how to read.

Plan B

B is for beautiful, and B is for brave. B is for bathing suit and begonias, blossom. B is for big and bountiful, for bougainvillea bursting. B is for bright. B is for bride, then blooming, then bleeding. B is for birth, for bouncing baby boy. B is for breasts. B is for broken nights, for broken bodies, for broken homes. B is for blood, for bruises. B is for bearing burdens. B is for breaking up and breaking down. B is for the bottom you hit after he hits you. B is for breaking free.

In the House of the Devil

Your pisco breath hot on my cheek, you push into me.

Through the window, I count the rooftops, until black swallows them, and I wonder how many other homes harbour secrets like magma.

Only tourists search the sky for the volcano here. The locals try to ignore it, though it tars the town, lake and everything in between with its name. In Mapuche, Villarica is *Rucapillán* or 'devil's house'.

I should have listened to their warnings.

In the morning, my skin and the sheets are streaked with your eruption.

You lie dormant.

Lava comes from the Latin verb to wash.

One for Sorrow

The first time I saw Mark raise his right hand, I winced. Salutes meant one thing in my experience, and after being married to a military man for half my life, they made me want to run a mile. And given the circumstances, that was ironic.

On second thoughts, perhaps he was just waving at someone he knew; after all, he seemed like a friendly sort. He had been the first person to greet me at the athletics track, and he was the one who suggested I tag along with his group for my first session with the running club.

But when he saluted again a mile or so later, I had to wonder if he had an ulterior motive. And with nobody else in sight apart from the group of us running, I thought it best to broach the subject. I could hear Jack's voice – my ex-husband's constant 'for fuck's sake, Karen', refrain in my head, as I imagined the headlines in tomorrow's papers: Divorcee gets duped by mass marathoning masked murderer.

'That's two,' said Mark, pre-empting my question. 'Two for joy.'

I didn't have a clue what he was talking about, but I wasn't going to jettison any little bit of lightness coming my way. Soon our feet fell into line, and I figured it couldn't hurt opening up a little, any more than it hurt having run this far already.

'What do the salutes mean?' I asked.

'Magpies,' he said, quick as a flash. 'It's bad luck to ignore them. It's the only superstition I've got.'

I'd forgotten how much easier it was sometimes running with someone. The only time Jack and I had run together, he'd spent the whole time criticising my running style, even though I was the one who'd run the marathons and not him. Slowly I regained my breath, and before I'd really registered, my watch buzzed to mark five miles.

'Three for a girl, four for a boy,' said Mark.

From behind us came a grunt.

'What utter bollocks,' said the young guy, who had been trailing us. 'Never heard such nonsense,' he blurted out and sprinted off to catch two other youngsters who had gone ahead.

'Don't worry about him; Testosterone Tony, we call him. He's not quite realised life is a marathon, not a sprint,' said Mark, his elbow grazing mine.

I knew I'd bitten off more than I could chew going with the faster group, but I had no intention of giving up and turning back now. I slowed my pace, then stopped to pretend to lace one of my shoes.

'So, what is it that brings you here?' Mark paused next to me, his breathing heavier than I expected.

I looked up, his legs long in Lycra, his top hugging his not-too-shabby figure. To our right, one, two more birds floated down to the water's edge.

'Five for silver, six for gold,' he said, apparently forgetting his question. He turned to me and smiled, and I felt the empty space on my left hand where my ring had been.

In the distance, the other runners had stopped by the metal fence to the sports centre, stretching languorously. On the bank between the wire and the water's edge, the fading sun caught something, and it glimmered like a mirror. Mark didn't see the bird dive towards the diamond light.

'What is it for seven?' I asked. 'Just in case?'

'Seven for a secret never to be told,' and I thought I saw him wink, but it could just have been a trick of the light.

Octopus

When my daughter asks, 'Am I your favourite?' I wrap my arms around her. Seconds later, her little brother says the same. They may only be half-siblings, but they share the same jealousies, the same abilities to wind each other up, to hurt, to love, to hold, to hinder, to say 'I hate you', though they do not know the weight of these words.

'An octopus has three hearts,' I tell them both, knowing this is the only way to a happily ever after. 'So that means you get one heart each and I don't have favourites.' I stroke my girl's long black hair which she once wished was red like mine, like the little mermaid. When she realised the choices Ariel made for love, she changed her mind. Next up was Snow White, but the idea of an evil stepmother was too close for comfort. Her father and his new wife are long gone now, but just occasionally, I hear her wondering about the whole new world he could offer her and try to ignore the fact she looks like Jasmine from Aladdin most of all. Now she flicks out her phone, pulls a pose I've still to master, and snaps a shot of us both against the sky, filtered and turquoise as the ocean.

Her reaction is too hard for a four-year-old to compute, and I sense his anger before I see him, steel myself to ease him with my embrace. Still, he charges towards us, unaware of the limited effort it takes to knock both his sister and me off balance, though she will right herself sooner.

'What about me?' he says, lacing his fingers through mine, holding my heart in his tiny hands. 'If an octopus has three hearts, that means I get one too?'

I nod, fixing the tea towel around his neck, loosely so it won't hurt but not so loose it will hook on something. He's obsessed with superheroes and magic but still too young to know the dangers of real life.

'But that's only two. What about your third heart?' He is standing on the sofa, arms raised beneath the kitchen cape, ready to fly, and I wonder when I stopped believing in magic. My anxiety bubbles to the surface, and I ready my arms. Perhaps if I had less love, I wouldn't worry so much.

His dad keeps on reading, one hand turning the pages, the other nursing his mug of tea. 'The third heart is for me,' says my husband, glancing up with a grin. His cup wobbles, spills, and I watch the slow-motion crash of our baby bouncing to the floor. He skids to a halt by his sister's feet, knocks her off balance so her phone smashes to the ground.

With one arm, I pick up my son, another my distraught daughter. With a third, I untie the tea towel. A fourth mops the spilt drink. Two more sweep up the phone. Eight arms may be enough, but three hearts mean there will never be enough love left for me.

The Girl from Ipanema

I remember the hush-hush of the water stroking the shore, the women with their toned, tanned legs and bare breasts scaffolding the favela sky. I remember watching the men watching the women watching the men with their tight trunks. I remember how my dad used to call them budgie smugglers and how I never quite understood why a man would choose to bury a bird down there. I remember following the women and the men away from the water, away from the hush-hush to the bam-bam of the samba and laughter. I remember the hot, soft slip of sand between my toes, wishing I had bought those Havaianas like everybody else, wishing my legs were long and lean, my breasts scaffolding but free. Then I remember the clink of glasses, the crystal kiss of strangers' cocktails – *Caipirinha, Carioca?* I remember shaking my head. *Obrigada. No. Eu não falo português. I'm not from around here.* I remember how he laughs, shakes his head and pushes the drink into my hand, *hush, you like this, no?* I remember the words of the song: the girl from this beach, Ipanema. I remember them, watching me watching them watching me.

Snow Angels

Let's say we made love for the first time in your den, downstairs from where your mom was baking in her Martha Stewart kitchen. The sweet smell of her cookies would wrap us in a blanket so warm it wouldn't matter that your Dodge Shadow would get snowed in that night and that we'd have to miss school the next day.

You would turn up the music, and the lines of that Garth Brooks song would inscribe themselves in my mind the way you scratched our initials into your bed's wooden frame. We would stay looped together in lyrics and lust, only unfastening ourselves when we heard your mom's footsteps on the stairs.

Then we would scramble for our high school debating shirts, throwing them on backwards. Your mom would knock to say she was leaving the milk and the cookies outside, like she wished we were seven but secretly knew we were seventeen. She would scarcely be on the stairs before you would fling open the door to the familiar smell of your childhood, which was foreign to me yet made me feel I had come home. You would follow her faltering footsteps with a furtive thanks thrown into the shadows and turn to tell me, 'You're like the daughter she never had.' By then, your mom would be on the back deck searching the sky for the one star she hunted for every night.

We would snuggle into your bed again, toes touching, limbs entwined like the tree branches that brushed the snow from the window.

Only later would our fingers feel for the last cookie crumbs, and our lips linger on the edge of kisses stained with milk.

When we'd wake from these delicious dreams, it would be to creep into the kitchen, where we would cram more cookies into our bodies, like animals preparing to hibernate. We'd tip-toe past my memory of your mom asleep in her recliner, your grandma's patchwork quilt pulled around her neck.

'Is that you?' she'd murmur, her head tilted to the stars. 'Hello, Ma,' you'd say, your chin following the line hers took.

DIY

The first thing Dad bought me after the divorce was a hammer. It came in a grey plastic toolbox, a bit like the kind a kid might ask Santa for at Christmas, with lips that clipped closed and kept the hammer, the spirit levels, the spanners and screwdrivers, all exactly where they were supposed to be.

I wanted to put some photos on the walls, populate the pale paper spaces where our portraits had once hung in a failed attempt at happy families. But the case was upside down, and when everything fell out, the hammer narrowly missed my foot. After that, I was too scared to use it, so the box lay in the utility room, behind the sachets of special offer cat food, and the sheets from Chloe's crib that had once been saved for a second baby but had since been recycled as dust covers.

I left the new photos of me and her, stacked like soldiers in their cheap Ikea frames between the sofa bed and the curtain for the next time Dad came to visit. I tried to ignore the divots in the wall I'd made one night when I had another go with the hammer after a couple of wines. The next day, Chloe tried to copy my marks by scribbling on the skirting board.

I'd not expected to see Dad again so soon; after all, he lived eight hours away, and his heart hadn't been good since Pete moved us from my childhood home.

~

At first, I think the man at the door is an Amazon delivery guy. But the envelope he hands me is far too thin to carry the DVDs I've ordered Chloe as a treat.

I close the door and fall to the wall as if pinned.

The next time my dad comes to visit, it is to come with me to court, where I will fight to keep my daughter. We're both antsy, but he offers to drive. It's a damp January day, the windows steamed up from our anxious breath, and even though the heater is on full, I can't get warm. I'm flicking through the radio channels for something, anything, to distract me. The travel news tells us there's a delay up ahead. The judge won't care for my apologies. An absent parent is an absent parent.

Neither of us realises Dad has cut up the guy behind until the car stops in front. The driver of the Peugeot rocks towards us, a can of Special Brew in one hand, waving a hammer in the other. I tell Dad to stay in the car, and I get out slowly, moving around the car like a lioness guarding her cubs. I'm shaking; so too is the man, but I know I have a secret weapon.

It isn't until much later that I even think to ask who the hell keeps a hammer in their car?

A Game of Two Halves

When the full-time whistle blows, she knows the game has only just begun.

She's spent the last ninety minutes feverishly praying for his side to win. She doesn't believe in God, but right now, she's willing to give faith a chance.

She creeps into her son's bedroom, kisses his angel cheeks, pushes the blonde cows-lick curl out of his eyes, and he murmurs. She smiles. Both son and father talk in their sleep, walk too sometimes.

The last time he'd been drinking, she woke up to find him pissing in the corner of the room, over the photo frame of the three of them he insisted on keeping there. Happy bloody families. Amazing how pictures can hide the horrible truth, the lies behind the smiles.

Johnny, it's okay, sweetheart, let's go to the toilet. She spoke to him like she was talking to their three-year-old, not a grown man.

He turned and grabbed her by the neck, tried to pin her to the bed. They say never wake a sleepwalker, but what if by letting him sleep, you let yourself die?

The whistle goes. Nil-nil. She guesses which of them will strike first.

Him.

Extra fucking time. They're not the only ones living on extra time. Oi, I'm talking to you. Come here.

She tiptoes in, invisible eggshells cracking.

Where's the rest of the beer? Didn't I tell you to get more in?

No point telling him that he'd drunk all of it, including the extra.

I'll go and get some more.

Damn right, you will. And don't you get chatting to any of your fancy men down there. I'll know if you have, you slut.

He hisses at her, lines pulsing in his temples like cerebral snakes.

She toys with the idea of running away then. She wants to tell the woman in Tesco that no, she's not enjoying the game when she nods knowingly at the beer. Mandy, her name is.

Between you and me, I'm glad to be out the house, Mandy explains.

It can get a bit lively when there's a game on. Let's hope it doesn't go to penalties, huh? I don't know that I can cope with the stress. Mind you, some ways are better than others, love, aren't they?

She winks and then bends to a fake whisper. *Nine months after the last World Cup, there were loads of babies born. Must be why they call it the Beautiful Game.*

She thinks of her son at home – her little boy born just as Mandy said. He's her reason she can't say anything. He's the reason she has to go back.

She nods, words forming under her tongue, desperately trying to escape. *I know what you mean,* is all she can brave.

She creeps up the stairs, struggling under the weight of the box of beer which she tries to balance on the coffee table.

What took you so long? He is livid. They're still only in the first half of extra-time, still no goals.

For a split second, it's as though he might help her. He rises up, takes her by the thin strap of her vest, pushes her back, and she falls forwards over the same coffee table, beer box breaking her fall.

What the hell did you do that for? They'll be too fizzy to drink now. Her right wrist is bruised. She's relieved, nothing worse.

Please don't let it go to penalties, she whispers silently.

What did you say?

But her answer is drowned out by the sudden scream of success, and she slinks away in the vacuum of short-lived victory.

She hears a noise from her son's bedroom, a nightmare played out in words she cannot understand. She curls up next to him, stroking his downy softness, kissing the damp patch on his neck where the sweat of bad dreams has clung to his pyjamas. He clings to his new pillow that he got for his third birthday a couple of months ago, a fluffy football in his team's colours.

The room explodes next door. Not them this time. The other side.

She looks at the clock on the wall, the black-and-white markings of another nod to the beautiful game. There are just seconds left.

The whistle goes.

She's made it through extra-time.

What the hell are you doing in there?

Just saying goodnight, she whispers. She kisses her son on his cheek, flushed pink with bad dreams. *It'll be alright, baby,* she whispers, pleading with him.

She moves his hands away from his fluffy football. She already knows the result of this game.

Quid Pro Quo

I'm sitting on the granite work surface in the kitchen, next to a rack of spices, when his phone rings. He draws up his boxers, wanders into the cream living room in just his underwear, and the cool stone beneath my thong makes me shudder.

I've never even heard of some of the spices here. Piment d'Espellete. Nigella Seed. Sumac. They are as foreign as the photo opposite: a canvas of him and his wife, their two white-blonde children, all laughing from a palm-fronded beach.

He's back in seconds, apologetic, aroused.

'It was the Desk. We've got a front page. See what I said about sticking with me.'

When he lowers me onto him against the counter, it's like nothing I've ever felt before. Afterwards, he quotes lyrics from Nick Drake, tells me I'm his 'Northern Sky', that he's never felt 'Magic Crazy' like this.

'We're only together for the kids.' I see the tears in his eyes, fight back my own.

We shower together in a wet room almost the size of my rented studio, then he makes me coffee from his Gaggia. The milk creams around the top of the tiny cup. He dips his finger in the froth and sucks it off my nipples. We have sex again, and he holds me so tightly after he comes that all I can do is stare straight ahead. I read the dates on the calendar, the doctor's appointments, the details of London Fashion Week, dinner at The Ivy. Next to them, the children's crayonings stick to the fridge with magnets from Val d'Isere, the British Virgin Islands.

Their Dear Daddy scribblings are signed with names like the offspring of Hollywood stars. They are names that will never sit behind the counter at Tesco, work double shifts at Wetherspoons, fight their way to being the single state school intern at the national newspaper. They are names that will never ask themselves how they ended up shivering on the kitchen surface of a married colleague's million-pound home, their fancy pants twisted around their ankles.

What Would Happen If a Leopard Could Change Its Spots?

She's flicking through one of those animal encyclopaedias, the kind you get heavily discounted in the run-up to Christmas. The kind nobody is ever going to pay full price for. 'Do you think I should keep this one, Mum?' she asks. 'I mean, it was a present. From him.' I shrug my shoulders. I learned long ago that she'll make her own decisions. Especially when it comes to her father. 'Look, why don't we have a hot chocolate. All this packing is making me thirsty. I got some marshmallows.' I catch myself in mid-sentence, remember how they told me that no attempt to compensate was ever going to make a difference. 'I'm fourteen, Mum,' she says. 'Remember. Not four. Still, if there's marshmallows, then maybe!' She's still thumbing the thick pages of the book blotted with stains from childhood spillages when I return, a tray of drinks and a plate of biscuits to sweeten the separation. 'Did you know that leopards only get together to mate?' she says, without looking up. I peer at my only child, feel a pang of loss at the fact that my little girl is now almost a young woman. 'God, if only things at school were so easy,' she groans. 'If we could avoid the boys all the time, until we were old enough to, you know...' I smile, wonder how long it will be until she gets her heart broken by the boy who just wants her for sex. I think about him. How he made a show of being the solitary beast, the man able to adapt to all kinds of environments, the man who ultimately just wanted to track me down, fuck and fight. 'It says,' she says, looking at me, a wide cocoa rim lipsticking her mouth. 'The leopard is a supreme hunter, known for its speed and power. Well, maybe that makes me half leopard then.' She laughs, her long legs sheathed in Lycra from our morning run. 'It is also known for its stealth? What exactly does stealth mean, Mum?' I think for a minute, twisting her long brown hair in my fingers, then holding it up against the light to catch a glimpse of gold. One day I will be able to get over the fact that she looks nothing like me, apart from the hidden highlights. 'It means when you do something so secretly, it catches someone by surprise,' I tell her. 'You mean like Dad?' she says, quick as a flash. I turn away, trying to hide my expression. When I turn back, I realise she has slipped the book silently into the box.

Bijihuanu

You are *Bijihuanu*. His mother gifts you this title, with the geometric terracotta-and-black skirt of his people. *It means Sparky*, he says, and you marvel at what she has bestowed. In Shipibo, his name means *born in a boat*, and you imagine him slipping from her, lithe as the anaconda stitched into the geography of his childhood and the geometry of your skirt. He unravels it, the fabric and the fables, until you are both naked beneath the Amazonian sky. Now he plucks leaves from heaven-grazing trees, pours vinegar and water into the poultice and places it to your lips. You wait for the bitterness, but there's only the sweet taste of something foreign but familiar. *Ayahuasca,* he chants, a perfect Peruvian lullaby: *Ayahuasca.* There are other words too in this sacred hymn he calls *Icaros*, and you recall that myth of a man who flew too close to the sun. But this man will never burn you. His eyes are deeper than the river, where you want to plunge your hungry soul. You follow him to the water's edge and bathe in the memory of somewhere you have never been. *Bijihuanu*, he whispers, the heavens humming with the sounds of his Amazon home. *Bijihuanu*, he repeats, and you call his name. The jungle listens and answers: cries and moans, half-human screeches in the dark, the hush, hush of water lapping, and somewhere out there, life beginning and ending on this endless river. You imagine the infant in the boat, now the man clinging to you as if he might drown in your being. In the dark, the walls of his world are mapped on your eyelids a heaven of stars brighter than you have ever seen. And you know this is what your name means. You fall asleep now in his arms and dream of the Amazon stroking your skin, an anaconda wrapping itself around you, and a baby unfurling like a fern from the forest.

ACKNOWLEDGEMENTS

Mum and Dad, you encouraged me to follow my dreams wherever they might take me, and were there when I stumbled. Thanks, Mum, for the glorious cover image. Terry, you believed in me, even when I didn't. Azara and Rafferty, you reminded me to stay grounded, but aim for the stars. I'm proud to be your Mum. Friends, who may not wish to be named, you helped me share my stories, even when that hurt, and you inspired some of these works. Amy and Vix, you accepted my stories, listened, and shared your own. Johanna, thanks for reading early versions of this collection and many of my pieces, and for suggestions to improve them.

Dave from Reflex believed in this collection from the beginning and patiently nurtured into its published form. I'm indebted to the lovely flash community for publishing my pieces, celebrating my successes, and picking me up. Vanessa Gebbie, thanks for introducing me to the concept of flash fiction. I'm grateful for your teaching and kindness, and to other teachers, Meg, Ken, Kathy, Tania, Nuala. Michael Loveday, you have my gratitude for patiently mentoring me to getting this collection completed and for the mind map now on my wall.

And finally, to the little girl who dreamed of being a writer, who was silenced from telling her own stories for years, it took a long time, but we got there. To you, and to any others who have felt the shame of silence, your voice matters.

The author and publisher wish to thank the editors of the journals in which the following stories were first published:

'Sarajevo Rose' was first published in *Restore to Factory Settings* (Bath Flash Fiction Award Anthology), December 2020; 'Behind the Mountains, More Mountains' – *Spelk*, March 2020; 'No Woman's Land' – *Cabinet of Heed*, August 2018; 'Bulletproof' – *Cabinet of Heed*, June 2020; 'Lesser Known Facts About Sloths' – *VirtualZine*, August 2019; 'Game Over' – *The Phare*, November 2020; 'The Huntsman' – *Rhythm & Bones*, December 2018; 'YOLO' – *EllipsisZine*, June 2020; 'Mother of Gold' – *Cabinet of Heed*, August 2019; 'There Are Twenty Million People in New York, but Tonight We Are the Only Two' – *Spelk*, April 2019; 'How Not to Make a Birth Plan' – *Cabinet of Heed*, December 2018; 'Iso – From the Greek Meaning Equal – Usually Used as a Prefix, i.e. Isolation, Isobar, Isopod' – *You are Not Alone: An Anthology of Hope and Isolation*, June 2020; 'How the Hostile Environment Instructor Failed to Teach Me About the Real Hostile Environment' – *Lunate Fiction*, August 2019; 'Before the Baby Was Born' – *Reflex Fiction*, November 2019; 'A List of All the Places I've Loved and Lost You' – *Lunate Fiction*, March 2020; 'Sunday Best' – *Storgy*, December 2019; 'Lady Bugs' – *Bending Genres*, June 2019; 'Jesus to a Child' – *Storgy*, December 2019; 'A Linguistic Theory of Bats' – *Restore to Factory Settings* (Bath Flash Fiction Award Anthology), June 2020; 'Birthday Girl' – *EllipsisZine*, March 2021; 'Drosophila melanogaster' – *X-R-A-Y Literary Magazine*, January 2020; 'No Place for a Girl' – *Reflex Fiction*, July 2019; 'The Toy' – *Flash Fiction Festival Anthology*, Autumn 2018; 'The Species of Pangolin Compromise Their Own Order: Pholidota' – *Restore to Factory Settings* (Bath Flash Fiction Award Anthology), June 2020; 'How Do You Classify Mammals?' – *Storgy*, July 2019;

'Birth Plan' – *EllipsisZine*, November 2019; 'Love Is Many Things, None of Them Logical' – *How to Hold an Umbrella* (Retreat West Flash Fiction Award Anthology), October 2020; 'Hooked' – *TSS Publishing*, August 2020; 'In the House of the Devil' – *Retreat West*, April 2020; 'One for Sorrow' – *Fiction Kitchen Berlin*, March 2020; 'The Girl from Ipanema' – *Flash Fiction Festival Anthology*, Summer 2019; 'Snow Angels' – *FlashFlood*, June 2019; 'DIY' – *Lunate Fiction*, January 2020; 'A Game of Two Halves' – *EllipsisZine*, July 2018; 'Quid Pro Quo' – *I'll Show You Mine Anthology*, March 2020; 'What Would Happen If a Leopard Could Change Its Spots?' – *Storgy*, March 2020; 'Bijihuanu' – *I Must Be Off!*, March 2020.

ALSO FROM REFLEX PRESS

Love Stories for Hectic People
Catherine McNamara

The thirty-three flash fictions of *Love Stories for Hectic People* explore the alignment of beings that is love. There is love that is vulgar, love that knows no reason; there is love that cradles the act of living, love that springs through the cracks; love that is slaughtered. These tales take place from Italy to Ghana to Greece and London and Tokyo, in grainy cities and muted hotel rooms; there is a Mafia murder, an ambulance rescue worker and a woman whose husband falls off a mountain. There is unchaste attraction and slippery, nuanced love; police violence and porn, and fishing too.

'*Catherine McNamara is one of the best writers I've read in all the time I've been in publishing.*'
—Christopher James, *Jellyfish Review*

'*Sharp, witty and deeply real, these small stories reveal moments of connections, and sometimes dissolution. One can't help but be captivated by these many and varied truths.*'
—Michelle Elvy, *the everrumble*

Some Days Are Better Than Ours
Barbara Byar

Some Days Are Better Than Ours is a startling collection that explores human life in all its forms. These stories will make you draw breath as you race through compelling accounts of the dark places people escape to and from.

Through her masterful use of language, Barbara Byar skilfully invites the reader into imagined futures and regretful pasts – from war to childhood to road trips to relationships. Her pieces are visceral, sometimes brutal but sliced through with hope. These stories, and the characters in them, strike straight at the realist heart of the human experience and will linger long after reading.

'These are searingly truthful fictions. Pitched at the border of poetry and prose, they catalogue lives lived at the edge, survivors facing the beauty and cruelty of the world. These fictions will take your breath away.'
—William Wall, *Suzy Suzy* and *Grace's Day*

'Barbara Byar writes flash like no one else; in each of these lucid and furious twenty-nine stories – some no longer than a single page – are wholly unforgettable glimpses into the lives of her individual characters.'
—Peter Jordan, *Calls to Distant Places*

REFLEX PRESS

Reflex Press is an independent publisher based in Abingdon, Oxfordshire, committed to publishing bold and innovative books by emerging authors from across the UK and beyond.

Since our inception in 2018, we have published award-winning short story collections, flash fiction anthologies, and novella-length fiction.

www.reflex.press
@reflexfiction